IN MY BOOTS

A year on a Lake District farm

IN MY BOOTS

A year on a Lake District farm

Andrea Meanwell

with photographs by Suzanne McNally

HAYLOFT PUBLISHING LTD.

First published Hayloft Publishing Ltd., 2017

A CIP catalogue record for this book is available from the British Library

ISBN 978-1-910237-35-9

Designed, printed and bound in the EU

Hayloft policy is to use papers that are natural, renewable and recyclable
products and made from wood grown in sustainable forests. The logging
and manufacturing processes are expected to conform to the
environmental regulations of the country of origin.

Hayloft Publishing Ltd,
a company registered in England number 4802586
2 Staveley Mill Yard, Staveley, Kendal, Cumbria, LA8 9LR (registered office)
L'Ancien Presbytère, 21460 Corsaint, France (editorial office)

Frontispiece: Lost in thought, Coniston Water,
photograph Suzanne McNally

Email: books@hayloft.eu
+44 (0) 7971 352473 (UK)
+33 (0) 380 89 760 (Fr)
www.hayloft.eu

For my family
Past, present and future

Contents

Introduction	8
Prologue	9
The Farm	10
January	11
February	23
March	28
April	35
May	45
June	55
July	63
August	76
September	85
October	98
November	106
December	114
Afterword	127
A Moment's Sadness	129
Hope in a Handful	130
Acknowledgements and references	131

Introduction

My family and I are blessed to live on a small Lakeland farm in the Rusland Valley. You may have read *A Native Breed* in which I explain how we came to live here.

In this book I hope to tell you about the different jobs that we do at different times of the year on the farm, how the seasons and weather affect our lives, and how we work with nature, not against it, to maintain the landscape of the Lake District. The book records the year 2016, on a small farm in the Lake District National Park.

Prologue

It's a beautifully sunny day and I am standing outside my house when my neighbour roars up on his quad bike.

'There's big trouble up at Mucky Puddle,' he shouts, 'what with these poachers, and gates being smashed, and the flooding down at The Strands, we're all up against it.'

He roars off again. A friend, visiting from Kendal, stands aghast. 'What on Earth was all that about?' he asks. I smile, it all made perfect sense to me. Living and working in our valley we have shared problems, our own way of referring to things that those who don't live and work here might wonder at; our own little world like any place of work.

This book is an invitation to work alongside me for a year.

The Farm

Resources at 1st January 2016:

    Traditional Cumbrian longhouse built circa 1565
    Small barn with two loose boxes and hayloft over
    Modern wooden hay barn 45 x 15 feet
    32 Rough Fell ewes
    3 Rough Fell tups
    22 Rough Fell gimmer hoggs
    16 Shetland ewes
    5 Shetland gimmer hoggs
    30 Hebridean/North Ronaldsay ewes
    8 gimmer hoggs
    5 Ouessant ewes
    1 Ouessant gimmer hogg
    5 Dexter cows
    4 Fell ponies
    2 Shetland ponies
    3 alpacas
    3 geese and 1 duck
    8 hens
    3 working border collies
    2 terriers
    60 acres rough grazing
    5½ acre hay meadow
    Rough fell grazing land
    14 year old Land Rover
    Small sheep trailer
    One woman, three sons and a working husband

January

T.S. Eliot said in *The Waste Land* (1922) that 'April is the cruellest month', but as you join us in the waste land that is Cumbria after the December floods and landslides of 2015, January seems to be the cruellest month.

Daylight is in short supply on the hill farm, and physical tasks are plenty. January always feels like a bit of an endurance exercise, something that must just be 'got through' in order to get to lambing and the brighter times of spring ahead. This January is additionally difficult in that there is a lot of clearing up to do after the extreme weather events of December.

On 6 December 2015 up to 341mm of rain fell in 24 hours in Cumbria, compared to the long-term monthly average for December in Cumbria of 173mm. We are well prepared for snow, but the landslides that occurred in Cumbria were something that could not have been prepared for. Thankfully our farm was not too badly affected. We had to go out in the middle of the night, with our head torches on, to knock down a wall opposite the house to allow floodwater to flow down the valley instead of into our kitchen.

Remarkably we had only one wall to repair, but several fences had been knocked down surrounding the small river Rusland Pool, which flows through our land.

It's the first Saturday afternoon in January, and my middle son Hector and I are attempting to fix some of the fencing. The wire has been pulled from its supporting posts, and is currently attached at one end with the wire in the river stretching several hundred meters downstream.

The water in the river is about twelve inches deep, enough to knock us off our feet as we have discovered, and we are both in the stream trying to untangle the fencing. I stand by the end that is anchored, trying to disassemble a small dam that has been built by debris carried along by floodwater. A pile of trees, branches and debris about four feet high has been built up around an old footbridge, and I'm standing in the river trying to remove this, while Hector untangles the wire. It takes us all afternoon to sort out, and rehang the fencing with sharp barbed pins that I pass to Hector and he hammers in. It is a job well done, and we go for a cup of tea satisfied with our work as it gets dark.

It feels good to work together and get a job done. Most of the month of January is spent in routine jobs. Sometimes during the summer I long for the routine of winter-feeding, but during winter it can seem like an endless grind.

The main source of animal food for the winter is the hay barn stacked with hay. The rate at which this diminishes is makes for a lot of contemplation and discussion. Bad weather, such as snow, will mean an increase in hay usage and this will be a cause for concern.

I measure out my expected usage per month and mark it out on the haystack with pairs of old sheep shears that are stuck into the bales. Each set of shears shows where we should be at the end of each month, and illustrates clearly how well we are doing.

Feeding the animals takes about four hours per day. I set off in the Land Rover and the first stop is the tups. These are the young male sheep that are being reserved for breeding in the future. They are living in a paddock at a holiday cottage in the valley. This is an excellent way to promote our local breed, the Rough Fell sheep, and the people who stay at the holiday cottage can feed the sheep if they'd like to.

We then head to our main block of land in the Crake Valley. On the way the dogs and I stop at our local agricultural supplier to buy sheep food. Sometimes these guys at the feed store will be the only people that I speak to during the day, a quick conversation about the weather is always welcome.

The road becomes quieter as we head into the Crake Valley. Through the village of Lowick and down a lane, we are really off the beaten track now. This is the real Lake District that few visitors and tourists will ever see. The road twists through scrubby woodland, with crags and boulders on either side of the lane. The Land Rover just fits through, but if it is icy this can be tricky as there is no way of seeing around corners to anticipate if anything else is coming. On route we usually encounter my neighbour's Highland cattle that will stand stoically in the road and then move off at a snail's pace; moving for the Land Rover is a great inconvenience to them.

The road appears to be at a dead end with a gate across the road that has to be opened. Blawith Fell reaches a height of 806 feet, is on the left and the hay meadow to the right. The lane is edged on both sides by hawthorn hedging, and the fields around us are separated by five feet high dry stone walls made of grey slate. The gimmer (girl) lambs that are being kept for breeding the following year will be on these hay meadows. As soon as they hear the Land Rover approaching they start to run the length of the field, baaing.

The sheep are very inpatient to be fed, and will jostle for position. As I fill up the buckets with feed and walk through the gate they sometimes knock me over in their rush to get to the food if I are not on my guard.

The gimmer lambs are fed with sugar beet pellets that are a good, high-energy food, as are the older in-lamb sheep. Every sheep has to be counted and checked. This is easily done when they are eating the sugar beet and, as they walk away from the sugar beet it's a good time to check if they are limping.

Foot problems are inherent at this time of year, particularly when it has been so wet. If a sheep is limping she will need to be caught, preferably on the very first day that she limps, and definitely within the first three days. Once she is caught she needs to be sat on her bottom with all four legs off the ground. She is then unable to move, and hopefully she will sit still. Her feet are cleaned and inspected.

If the sheep has foot rot it is obvious as soon as she is lifted up, as the foot will have an obnoxious smell. The foot may need to be trimmed; I carry a pair of sheep foot rot shears in my pocket, and then treat with an antibacterial spray. I use an herbal antibacterial spray, and then usually seal the foot with an iodine spray.

There are several different foot problems that can occur, and the shepherd becomes adept at identifying them and treating them with experience. Few problems will warrant a vet's call out; the shepherd must be able to deal with problems 'on the hoof'!

During the unusually wet spell in December/January we had several problems with pneumonia. Again the shepherd must be able to spot potential pneumonia. The first sign is

Waiting to be fed

usually that the sheep will become withdrawn and disinterested in food. We lost four lambs to pneumonia during the storms, so this year we decide to vaccinate our lambs early for pneumonia. Normally they would receive their booster injection in March, but this year it is moved forward.

The lambs must be held in a pen. This is thankfully easy during the winter. The sheep and lambs enjoy a bale of hay in a hayrack each morning. A pen can be made from interlocking metal hurdles and set up around the hayrack, and closed once all the lambs are eating. We vaccinate all the lambs in turn inside this pen, and give them a dose of wormer while we have them in. This will save us catching them again next week to do this, all the sheep have a dose of wormer and flukicide in mid-January to keep them in good health. We mark each lamb once it has been treated with a bright pink mark on her head, then there is no danger of catching the same lamb twice. A double dose of wormer would not be too disastrous, but a double dose of vaccine could kill.

One lamb that is down with pneumonia is living in the hay barn, eating hay ad lib. He has been named Lazarus, as I thought he was dead when he first went down with pneumonia, but while carrying him on my shoulders I realised he was actually alive. It will be a long road to recovery.

We then drive over Bessy Bank, back into the Rusland Valley. This is a steep road and if there is a risk of ice we choose an alternative, longer route. On the drive I try to listen to the radio, but the combination of poor radio reception and an old radio in the Land Rover usually results in a lot of buzzing and not a lot of listening. The vents on the front of the Land Rover are also stuck open, letting blasts of cold air across my legs while I am driving. An elaborate system of wrapping myself up in fleece scarves keeps me warm.

One morning I have an unfortunate accident when I get my phone out of my pocket to take a photo after driving, but my hands are frozen in the position they were on the steering wheel, and the mobile phone smashes on the floor shattering the screen. I am unable even to pick it up off the floor, as my hands simply will not work.

Once back in Rusland the first animals we encounter are the herd of fell ponies. These are semi-wild and engaged in rush removal. Their main food over winter will be acres of rush, supplemented as little as possible to encourage the rush removal. If it is snowing they will be fed a little hay. Each day in the snow they will each get a section of hay, and while they eat it I will be able to check them over and make sure that they are not losing any of their body condition.

Once we are happy that the fell ponies are well we will look for the North Ronaldsay sheep, and feed them a little hay or sugar beet so that we can check them too. It is very difficult to catch the North Ronaldsay sheep in the summer months because they are very suspicious of people and have no flocking instinct. During the early winter the male lambs will be caught and sold for breeding or meat, and the female lambs will be caught and taken to the hay meadow to overwinter.

They cannot be left with their mothers, as it is very important that they do not come into contact with the tup and get pregnant. If a lamb gets pregnant in her first year she will not have the opportunity to grow properly and achieve her full potential as a breeding ewe. The tup is also their father so any inbreeding must be avoided.

We then drive around to the Dexter cattle who will be waiting for their hay and feed. They enjoy routine and are impatient to be fed. There can be a lot of jostling and pushing for food, so I feed the cows over the wall and do not go in with them if I am on my own – safety must be the top priority. Along with the cows are the Hebridean sheep. They can be fed in a small orchard that the cows cannot get into, to make sure that they have adequate feed and it is not all gobbled by the cows. Finally we feed the Ouessant sheep and then the poultry. I do not usually take my dogs amongst the pregnant sheep if I can avoid it, so then there are five dogs to walk.

After feeding, walking and lunch, if no problems occur, there is then time to work on winter jobs such as walling, and before long it is starting to get dark. Before dark the dogs must be walked again, and at dusk the poultry are shut into their houses for the night. January is a month of work, but each day takes us a step closer to spring, and to lambing.

Most of the land seems to be hibernating throughout January with very little growth. The hayseeds that fall from the hayrack as the sheep eat will help to reseed the meadow, and help to feed the birds that overwinter here. The manure from the sheep on the meadows will help to fertilize the field and encourage grass growth in the spring. Even though the land is to all intents sleeping, it is repairing itself and gathering strength for the summer. Rest is important; it is part of the cycle of life for all living things. Our period of rest here in the Lakeland fells is much longer than in other areas, our growing season very short, but our animals and people will be strong having lived through the bitter winters in the fells.

The wet weather has also made things difficult for wildlife in the valley. The familiar figure of the barn owl hunting over the meadows at night is now often seen in the daytime, desperately looking for food. Deer in the valley are venturing into domestic gardens and causing chaos eating shrubbery, causing frustration to homeowners. There have been occasional sightings of young red kites; these were released into the valley as part of a plan to reintroduce them to Grizedale Forest.

My daily routine is well known by my companion 'Mr Robin' who will be waiting by the fell ponies when I return to the valley in the morning and will then follow me as I feed the animals and walk the dogs. He will then hop about on the windowsill outside the kitchen, as long as no cats are about, waiting for his birdseed. It is believed that robins used to follow wild boars around, getting food from the ground that they had turned over, and then took to following people after the extinction of the boar. This little robin certainly seems to have formed a strong bond with me.

I haven't actually seen a fox or a badger this month, but I have seen evidence of the badger. One morning when arriving to feed the North Ronaldsay sheep one of the shearlings was missing. I had fed her the day before. A search of the field found a skull, a backbone and a bit of fleece. The rest had been well and truly devoured by the badger. He must have sensed her weakness and attacked her, or perhaps she died suddenly and he came across her in the field. Either way, he had enjoyed a good feed at a sparse time of year. There is no point in being other than philosophical about this. We must work with nature, not fight against it, as to do this would be to fight a losing battle.

The hedgerows are bare at this time of year, with a clear view through some of them that can be tempting for a sheep to try and push through. The method of cutting hedgerows with a tractor instead of laying them traditionally has meant that the hedges have become too leggy, there are not enough branches going horizontally across the hedge. It will be a big job to re-lay the hedges rather then trimming them and it's not a job for this year. Part of living on a farm is learning to accept that your work will never be done. It is a continuous process of reviewing the jobs that could be

Feeding sheep self-service

done, and deciding which should be prioritized. There will never be nothing to do. Dark nights afford few opportunities for jobs to be done during the evenings.

At the end of January there is our annual social event with the Rough Fell Sheep Breeders' Association. This is a two-day event that is eagerly anticipated. On the last Friday in January there is a social event with a hot pot supper. As well as the meal there will be a charity auction. The entertainment usually includes stock judging where one of the breeders will bring along a group of their best sheep and everybody will have a go at placing them in order of merit according to the breed standard established by the association in 1926. A judge will then give his opinion, and those who agree with him will then have to guess the weight of the sheep, with the closest to the actual weight winning a prize.

Other entertainments include a photographic competition, a charity auction, spot the dog competition, name the dog competition, etc. A good time is had by all before the serious business of the in-lamb sale the following day.

The Rough Diamond sale is a sale of individual in-lamb sheep that are highly prized. There will typically be around 70 sheep for sale, and it is a chance to buy a different bloodline into your flock, perhaps in the hope of buying a sheep that will have a good tup lamb. Prices will range from around £100 to £600 per sheep. The sheep will be shown first and the prizewinners will usually attract the highest prices.

In 2016 the auction and the in-lamb sale were both held at NW Auctions near Kendal. In the charity auction I managed to buy two big stacks and two individual copies of the

Rough Fell Sheep flock book, from the 1970s and 1980s. These are issued annually by each breed society, listing their members and the tups and ewes that they own and register that year.

My own family history is recorded in the Swaledale Sheep Society flock books that sit on my bookshelves in the farmhouse. I can see the size of my uncle's flock growing each year as he registers more sheep. I would like to think that in years to come somebody will research my life through the Rough Fell Sheep Society flock books.

On the morning of the Rough Diamond sale we were running a little late, due to not getting to bed until the early hours the night before. We only had a quick look at the sheep before the sale, and one immediately stood out for me. 'That's the one,' I said to my son, and he noted the lot number in the catalogue.

The sheep I had spotted was a gimmer hogg, a young sheep not yet a year old. I had been attracted by the way it stood, its spotty legs with 'knee pads', and its face. Gimmer hoggs follow the in-lamb sheep into the ring, so the older sheep were up first. The top price was £500 for an individual sheep. I was really pleased to buy the sheep that I liked for £60 – a bargain. It will be interesting to see how she grows. At the end of January it's still raining. All is saturated. The rain seems endless. We can only hope for better drier days in February.

February

February begins as January ends, wet. The days are measured out in three pairs of waterproofs; morning, afternoon and evening. To compound the problem our air source heat pump has ceased to pump water around the under floor heating system, so it is very difficult to get things dry.

The daily routine of feeding continues, with rations gradually increasing as the ewes get nearer to lambing time. Mid-way through the month we assess the situation with the hay and decide to order in some silage for the cows. A neighbour is selling large bales of silage for £15, and will deliver them for an additional £2.50 per bale. The deal is soon sorted and the cows are very happy with the silage.

Six weeks before lambing all the ewes need a vaccination that will protect them from tetanus and a variety of sheep diseases. If given at the right time it will also protect their lambs for the first few weeks of their lives. The money earned from the sale of last year's boy lambs has now been spent, so in order to get the money to buy the medication I sell some flock books. They are flock books from the Oxford Down breed of sheep that I had bought before Christmas from eBay for £3 each. I contact the secretary of the Oxford Down Sheep Breeders' Association and somebody gets in touch with me who is interested in flock books. We agree on a price per book of between £20 and £50, depending on the age of the book, and this pays for the vaccinations.

February is also a time of taking stock of equipment, and assessing what will be needed for the coming year. We have been looking for a cattle crush for about six months, following on from an incident I had with a cow in the summer. We find one online and go to view it at a farm near Bassenthwaite. A price is agreed and it is delivered the following weekend.

We also go to a machinery sale and buy some interesting old tools. Included in the lots are a paraffin lamp that my youngest son Fergus loves, and a clipping stool. This is a coffee table sized stool that the sheep is laid on to shear sheep by hand. The shearer sits on the end. I have been looking for one of these for ages; it will make shearing the rare breed sheep a lot easier on my back. The rare breed sheep need to be hand clipped so that there are no 'second cuts', short bits of wool mixed in with the fleece. These are the bane of hand spinners.

February is also a good month for thinking about land management as the land is stripped totally bare. We would like to produce more hay, and are in discussions with a neighbour who is wishing to retire, to purchase two more fields. During the month she changes her mind about which fields she wishes to sell, but by the end of the month we have agreed on one small meadow for hay and one for rough grazing. Both fields will need fencing.

The area of rough grazing also requires some work as there is a lot of scrub to be removed. This will involve cutting off the scrubby bushes with a chain saw, and uprooting the stump by attaching a chain to it and pulling it out with the Land Rover.

There are some very large oak trees that will provide

Feeding sheep – photograph by Suzanne McNally.

lovely shade for the animals in summer, and little owls nesting in the field. The seller stipulates that the trees must not be removed, she emphasises that she is only considering selling us the land because she knows that we will not remove the trees and will provide habitats for wildlife.

In the middle of February, with six weeks to go before lambing, the hoggs (last years lambs – teenagers!) that have been retained for breeding next year need to move off the hay meadows to allow the grass to grow. The lambs will be born on a meadow so it is very important that there is a good supply of grass there so that the ewes have plenty to eat in order to provide their lambs with good quality milk. As the lambs are to be born and raised outside their nutritional requirements will also be higher than those born and raised indoors.

Photograph by Suzanne McNally.

The hoggs are moved into the rough grazing and are reunited with their mothers for the first time since weaning. There are a large number of sheep together now, and for the first couple of days after the move it is chaos at feeding time. The hoggs frantically look for their friends amongst the flock once they have eaten. Interestingly, they do not reunite immediately with their mothers. Some of the hoggs have never been in this area of grazing before, so I keep a close eye on them in case they get stuck in rushes or boggy areas.

We are blessed with three days of sun in the middle of February, which assists greatly with all this moving about. It also gives the dogs a run out with the sheep and they enjoy the challenge of moving the hoggs.

We spend a lot of the month of February thinking about my grandad who is critically ill in hospital in Durham. When we visit, in a rare lucid moment he tells Hector to 'look after the sheep, and take care of your mum.' Sheep first, as always. Aside from his interest in sheep, my granddad was an steam engine driver. He could talk all day telling stories about life on the engine footplate, and it is a great sadness that he is not able to see the restored *Flying Scotsman* as it steams along the Settle-Carlisle line. He drove this engine and was hoping to see it restored and running again.

February is another month to be 'got through'. Half an eye is on our hay supplies, and half an eye on the coming spring and lambing. Spring cannot come soon enough.

March

In March my grandad died. He had lain ill for several weeks and this exacerbated the feeling that winter has been going on forever. We lose our link with farming in the past, and we must remember and pass on all his stories. My father, husband and two elder sons carry the coffin into the packed church, and I read a lesson about lifting our eyes to the hills, for it is from there that strength comes.

Strength has been needed this winter, strength of character to see the winter-feeding through. It is no easy task to walk across a field carrying a hay bale on your back like a rucksack in strong wind, and we have had so many windy days of late.

Looking forward to lambing I order in supplies of ear tags for all the new lambs that we are expecting. We ear tag the lambs shortly after birth. It is a legal requirement to tag them, and we have found that it appears to be less painful to tag them when they are very tiny, and the ear grows around the tag, which is less likely to tear if it catches on a bush or fence. The smell of the plastic tags is also supposed to be off-putting to a fox.

This year our tags will be pink. I change the colour each year so that it is easy to identify a sheep's age at a glance. One of the tags, which holds the microchip has to be yellow and the other colour can be chosen. The tags have our flock number on them, a sheep's individual number, our name and farm name. Hector's lambs are ordered blue ear tags, again making them easy to identify. The ear tags cost about one pound per lamb. You can buy systems that record the growth, breeding, etc. of the lamb using the electronic ear tag, but we are unlikely to be able to afford equipment like this until it becomes much cheaper as the technology advances.

With the acquisition of more land our hay production will hopefully be stepped up in the summer. Last summer Hector asked a neighbour to cut and bale our hay. He worked with them cutting their own hay, and the cost of his labour was taken off the cost of producing our hay. It worked out at about one pound per small bale of hay. Hector is keen to help out again with hay making, and produce as much of our own hay by ourselves as possible, so he is looking out for second hand hay making equipment.

After several false starts he saw a Leyland tractor at £1,600 advertised online that he liked. We went to have a look at it, and he agreed to buy it, but the vendor phoned before he delivered it to say that there was a fault that would cost £500 to fix, so he decided to let that one go.

Although it is still bitterly cold in the last week of March, frogspawn appears littered all over the hay meadow. Spring must be on the way, although on higher ground winter still holds the ground in 'lockdown'. Nothing grows or flowers, but hares running across our fields carry the promise of spring by the spring in their step.

On the last weekend in March we gather all the sheep in for a sheep MOT before lambing. The younger sheep, hoggs that have been retained for breeding, are separated from the pregnant sheep. The hoggs have a pedicure and are sent back into the area of rough grazing where they live.

The pregnant sheep are moved onto the hay meadow to lamb. Not only is there better grass here, it is also much easier to check on who is lambing when the sheep are in a confined area. Forty-six sheep are put onto a five and a half

First lamb

acre field and another twenty into a smaller area. The Ouessants are brought inside. Their lambs are too tiny and vulnerable to be born outside and will be in danger from foxes.

Lambing pens are set up. The Rough Fell pens are put into the hay barn, and consist of four aluminium hurdles with an aluminium hayrack and bucket for water. Thankfully we still have some hay to feed them. The Ouessant hurdles are traditional wooden hurdles, fastened together with bailer twine. It is a timeless scene.

On 27 March primroses begin to flower in the hedgerows. Around our hay meadows there is an absolute profusion of primroses, unlike a lot of the Lake District where they have all but disappeared, reputedly removed by visitors to the area to take home. The primroses are also the food plant for the rare Duke of Burgundy butterfly that lives in this area. This is a small, springtime butterfly that lives on scrubby grassland and is one of the most rapidly declining butterflies in the UK.

Lambing should start on the 28 March, timed to coincide with the school Easter holidays. On that day we all drive to the hay meadows with an air of optimism and expectation, and yes, there is our first lamb of the year stood waiting for us in the watery sunshine of the early morning.

It is a black lamb out of a black Shetland sheep that we bred ourselves. We know that she is an excellent mother, so we ear tag the lamb, mark it with our purple flock mark and a dot of red to show that she is a little girl, a gimmer lamb. The lambs are marked red or blue for a boy or a girl, so that we know which lambs are boys to catch and castrate them.

There is no reason for the lamb and sheep to go inside,

so we move them through into the area of rough grazing together. They wander off together happily, a little team; one down, 45 to go. The lamb is recorded in our lambing records. Interestingly, she was the first sheep to lamb last year as well. There is snow on the high fells, but there is a newborn lamb with her mother in the sunshine. Spring must be on its way.

Two Rough Fell sheep lamb on the last day of March. It is so cold that despite being healthy and alert we put them inside in the pens in the hay barn to bond with their mothers. It is quite a physical job lifting the sheep up into the back of the Land Rover to drive them over to the barn. Rough Fells are the largest breed of mountain sheep. I put the lambs into the back of the Land Rover first, where the sheep can see them, and then attempt to lift the sheep in with them. I can lift most, but not all of my sheep, some are too heavy. When we reach the barn I carry the lambs so that the sheep can see them, and put them into a pen. Their mother then jumps out of the back of the Land Rover and follows them into the pen. A better system would be to have a quad bike with a small trailer, but funds do not allow for this at the moment.

The first 24 hours are crucial, as the ewe cannot recognise her own lambs at first until she has learnt their smell. She can be easily confused and may not realise she has twins, allowing another broody sheep to steal one. Generally though, Rough Fell sheep are excellent very alert mothers, and the lambs are lively and looking for milk instinctively immediately after being born.

Two days later the lambs go outside with their mothers. They are given plastic raincoats to wear to keep them warm and dry. The weather is relentlessly wet now, and we have to hope that our lambs are strong enough to survive the Cumbrian climate. The forecast for the coming two weeks when most of our lambs should be born does not look good, we have to hope that we too are strong enough to survive

whatever may be coming, fuelled by as much tea and flap-jack as we can consume between jobs.

The most mentally exhausting time of the year is upon us, a month that will see me waking and sleeping at odd hours and driving the school run with overalls on over py-jamas. There will be dramas, catastrophes and regrets with reruns of scenarios playing out in my mind, but this is what drives us, this is the time when we feel most alive and ut-terly exhausted at the same time. This is lambing.

April

April is not the cruellest month on a hill farm. It is the most exhilarating, heart stopping, exhausting and life-affirming month. April is entirely given over to lambing, by that I mean every waking or sleeping moment is monopolised by lambing or thoughts and dreams of lambing.

The day starts at 6am when the 'orphan lambs' are fed, the sheep inside fed and checked, and the puppies that are born to my working Border collie Moss are checked. Moss herself is given a short walk and an early breakfast. Mothers and babies are top priority in April.

No other activities or social engagements can be considered during April, it is a 24 hours a day seven days a week job lambing. After breakfast we drive around each of the areas where we have sheep. The ewes are fed. While they are distracted this gives us a chance to check the lambs. Often they have problems with pooey bottoms that need to be washed and dried with an old towel. The back of the Land Rover is stacked with towels in anticipation.

Once the mob of sheep in each field has been fed we can look for sheep that are lambing. A quick head count will have told us how many sheep have not come over to be fed. It can be difficult to count sheep that are jostling about, I always count them in threes, I find this is the easiest way.

Sheep that are missing will either be lambing, or will have lambed recently. If they are in the process of lambing we will stand back and observe. Our instinct and experience will tell us if and when we need to intervene. A sheep with a head sticking out from its rear end, or heaven forbid a leg, will be given just a couple of minutes benefit of the doubt, then helped to lamb by us. We do not know how long the sheep has been like this so we must act quickly. In the case of just one leg sticking out, we will intervene immediately. What we hope to see is a nose and two feet coming first.

Usually we are lucky enough to find a mother and her newborn getting to know each other. Native sheep can usually lamb unaided. It is important not to move the new family from the spot on which they were born, unless the weather is terrible and they need to go inside, as staying on that spot will help with the bonding process.

We quietly approach the sheep. Most of the sheep are quite happy to let us touch their lambs, as they trust us. Lambs will be picked up and checked to see if they have a full tummy of milk, ear tagged and tailed. Taking the bottom off their tails by placing a rubber band around it will prevent blowflies from attacking the tail in the summer. This infestation is most unpleasant for the sheep, far better to have the bottom of the tail taken off now and avoid maggot infestation.

Most mothers are able to lamb unaided and feed their young successfully requiring little help from us. They are moved off the meadow and into the rough grazing once feeding is established.

There are cows and ponies to be fed and checked, and dogs to be walked. These jobs are usually finished by 1pm for lunch. After lunch I usually have an hour's sleep during lambing, while the boys relax watching television.

The whole process begins again; everyone is checked again during the afternoon. The sheep know that they are not going to be fed during the afternoon so they do not bother to rush over to me. It is a good time to observe them with their lambs and check that no lambs are separated from their mothers.

Every day somebody will be separated. Having noticed a lamb unattended and shouting we will then need to find its mother. Once we have located the mother we walk really close to her. This will make her call her lamb and realise that it is missing. We then attempt to guide the sheep and the lamb towards each other. It is a tedious process and as it goes dark at 9pm we finally have everyone settled for the night. We then need to walk the dogs again, and keep busy and awake until the midnight feed of the orphan lambs. These are lambs that for one reason or another are not being fed by their mother. Sometimes a ewe will reject a lamb for no apparent reason, or she may believe she has only a single lamb when she has twins. We have never had a sheep with triplets, but if we did one of the lambs would have to be taken off her, as she would not have enough milk for three.

Depending on the age of the lambs they may need to be fed as often as every two hours. This will require setting the alarm clock for 2am and 4am and going outside with overalls on over pyjamas. Once the lambs are over a week old they can be taught to feed themselves from a bucket with teats on. Life becomes easier then, as the lambs do not need to be bottle fed individually.

This year we initially have three orphan lambs. Two

twins that a mother would not let feed, and a third orphan lamb donated by a friend. One of the twins did not survive their mother's neglect, and so there are two. It's a lot of

Carrying a pair of Rough Fell lambs.

work getting up in the night to feed two orphan lambs, so I buy another four from a breeder. These are girls and will be able to join the flock when they are older, so the expense of the milk and the hours put in will be justified. Some people do not breed from orphan lambs as they believe that they will be terrible mothers themselves, but we have not found that.

Other Rough Fell sheep needing extra attention include The Lamb Snatcher. We know that once she has lambed her hormones will tell her to accumulate other lambs, the first year she ended up with five lambs at one point. As soon as she has lambed we put her inside this year. Being confined to a small pen with only her own lambs will hopefully make her bond with only them. Much to her disgust, it seems to work.

She has a very distinctive face and I can spot her and her lambs at a distance of a couple of hundred yards. Throughout April I keep a very close watch on her, and the confinement has worked.

Other sheep need to be confined for different reasons. One has a bad case of conjunctivitis, and is temporarily blind. She is confined with her lamb while the medicines for her eye problem take effect. Twice I try her loose in the barn with her lamb, and it is obvious she simply cannot see her lamb, and panics, rushing around the barn crashing into walls, so back in the pen she goes. She is in there for two weeks, much to her annoyance, but at the end of two weeks she can see and is able to take her lamb outside. She loves her lamb, and they are able to live happily together outside.

Other sheep do not have such a success story. Two sheep are of questionable character, and are in the last chance saloon. Both abandoned their lambs last year, but for some reason we have given them the benefit of the doubt.

They are both confined with their lambs for a week before they are left outside with them. In a heartbreaking series of events they manage to both lose their lambs again. They are bad mothers, and will not have a future in the flock. They are taken to the auction the following week and sold for meat. This may seem harsh, but these sheep have now put lamb's lives in peril for two consecutive years. They are not suitable for breeding, so become part of the food chain.

The Hebridean sheep lamb well to the Ryeland tup. At the end of April we have twenty lambs from twenty sheep. One sheep lost her lamb, reason unknown, and one had twins. They have all lambed without assistance, and I have managed to catch and tag each newborn lamb and record its parentage in my record book. Some of the female lambs will be kept as breeding mules, a Ryeland/Hebridean cross.

The North Ronaldsay sheep have mixed fortunes. Two uncatchable sheep that I was unable to move into a paddock closer to home for lambing have a lamb each, and are living at large with the fell ponies. The two North Ronaldsay sheep that I could catch (after three weeks of feeding them in a pen and trying to catch them in there) are moved to a little field just behind the house. One has a boy lamb that I am really chuffed with, a potential show winner I am sure, but the other who is my favourite ewe does not lamb. I attribute this to the terrible weather during tupping time, and will give her another chance to breed next year.

That only leaves the Ouessants. Ouessants are the world's smallest breed of sheep, but despite that we have never had one that has had trouble lambing. Our new Ouessant tup has been bought from a farm in the Northern Lake District and is a lovely caramel colour.

The Ouessant lambs are so tiny that they are in danger of dying through being eaten by a predator or drowning during the first two weeks of their life. We have learnt this through painful experience, so they come into the barn to lamb. They could theoretically be the first sheep to lamb as their tup went in first, but we know from experience that they will probably be the last to start lambing.

We didn't have long to wait this year, though, as my white Ouessant ewe Stella had a healthy boy lamb on 6 April. Stella is precious as she was the very first lamb that we had born here at The Syke. The new arrival is also precious as he is a beautiful caramel colour. On the day he is born I send a photograph of him to a zoo in Lancashire that collects miniature sheep, and they agree to buy him in August once he is old enough to be weaned from his mother.

All appears to be going well, until when feeding the Ouessants at 10pm one night I notice a leg sticking out from the back of a young ewe. Quickly I investigate, and the lamb that is trying to come out is stuck fast. Hector and I try for twenty minutes to free the lamb, but its head is tucked into such a strange position inside the tiny sheep that I cannot move it.

We put the sheep into the back of the Land Rover and drive to our neighbour's for a second opinion. He is in the middle of lambing himself, looks at the size of the sheep lambing and simply says 'Bloody Hell Annie'. I ask about calling the vet, but he tells me that if I can get my (very small) hand inside the very small sheep that is more than the vet will be able to do, and I had better get on and lamb it myself.

So in pitch darkness I'm standing in my friend's farm-yard giving a running commentary on what is going on inside the sheep:

'I can feel its head. It's here.'

'Are you sure?'

'Yes, I've got my finger in its mouth now.'

'Bloody hell.' And so on. With my arm going further and further into the sheep and him pushing my sleeve further and further up, I have to feel each part of the lamb to bring its head and its feet round into line so it can be safely delivered.

'I'm sure it's dead.'

'It might not be, just get it out and we can have a look.' Eventually the tiniest lamb is pulled out into the back of the Land Rover. We all stare at the skinny blob, when suddenly it shakes its ears and tries to lift its head up.

'It's alive, its alive!' says my friend, and we all laugh.

The lamb is wrapped in a warm towel, and lamb and sheep are taken home and put under a heat lamp. The ewe is giving more cause for concern, she is exhausted. Once the ewe and lamb appear to be settled in the barn, we get back in the Land Rover to drive around to the house. It is now 1am. The engine of the Land Rover is running while we close the barn doors, and suddenly it locks itself shut with us outside. We do not have a spare key.

For a couple of minutes we stand there staring in disbelief looking at the Land Rover with its engine chugging away and all the doors locked. It has a full tank of petrol and it will take several hours to empty. Hector says it will

Photograph by Suzanne McNally.

be bad for the engine if we let it do that anyway, and sets about getting a long piece of wire and feeding it through the door seal to try and open the window by pressing the button with wire.

At 2am we let out an enormous cheer as he opens the window after painstakingly manoeuvring pieces of wire for an hour. It became a challenge that had to be completed. Thankfully that night I do not have to set my alarm for the 2am feed as I'm already up. There are always advantages to inconveniences.

The remaining Ouessants lamb without incident. I go over to my neighbour's to apologise for needing help, saying that in my six years of lambing I have never seen anything like a lamb that was so stuck. My neighbour replies that in his 35 years of lambing he has never seen anything like it either, so I mustn't worry.

While I am fully occupied bringing new life into the world and trying to keep all of it alive, Hector is still interested in buying a tractor with his inheritance from his great grand-dad. As a break from lambing we go to look at one on a Saturday afternoon near Kirkby Stephen. The seller gives my sixteen year old and my twelve year old the key and tells them to test drive it.

'How far shall we go?' they ask

'Stop when you get to Yorkshire' he replies.

Fergus's eyes open wide, until he explains that the county boundary is at the edge of the next field. We agree to buy the old Leyland on condition that one small problem is rectified, and return home optimistic. Two weeks later we receive the disappointing news that the tractor cannot be fixed, it is a more serious problem than was thought. We are still tractorless.

On the last day of April, with most of the lambs safely delivered and outside in the rough grazing, we wake up to snow. Sometimes the elements appear to be conspiring against you in farming and the weather this year has been exceptionally bad. We are still hopeful of a good summer, and looking forward to the agricultural shows that we will compete in.

May

May begins with sleety snow falling on newborn lambs. I battle the wind across the fields, trying to keep the lambs warm and dry by putting plastic macs on them. On the 1st May an older Rough Fell ewe has two tiny lambs. Try as I might I cannot persuade her to come into the building with them, and as I am on my own I cannot lift her into the back of the Land Rover as she is so heavy and cantankerous. I leave them outside and hope for the best, but by the end of the day, one of the lambs has died. I am furious with myself for not being strong enough to lift her, and furious with the weather for snowing heavily in May.

Fury has to set aside, there is too much to do. My sons have returned to university, agricultural college and school, so I am on my own during the day and must keep calm and carry on. On 2nd May the puppies are now a month old, and I decide to advertise them online. Much as I would love to we will not be keeping any of the puppies and I must find some suitable homes for them.

There are five puppies to sell and within 24 hours three are reserved with deposits. One lady who trains dogs for agility competitions insists on driving from Lincoln to the Lake District immediately the advert is posted in order to have the first pick of the puppies. She messages me within half an hour of the advert going live saying she is heading north, and can I text her my postcode. Four hours after the advert appears online she jumps out of her car after driving non-stop from Lincoln, and visibly collapses with relief when she sees the puppies saying, 'Thank goodness I have found one.' At last we are producing something that people are falling over themselves to buy.

All the puppies find homes easily, and it is lovely to meet their families and hear their plans for the dogs. We will be kept in touch of their achievements in the future, but throughout May I email them photos every couple of days to show how the puppies are growing. The puppies are socialised and hear a variety of noises including Radio 4, and meet lots of new people and dogs.

They are taken to the vets in the car to be microchipped and they are all sick in turn. They have a lot of learning to do before they go to their new homes. In the evenings we teach them their names, and to walk alongside us off lead.

Photograph by Fergus Meanwell.

Breeding puppies in an absolute joy, and I love seeing them develop. It is a very sad day when they leave.

Meanwhile in the midst of puppy training another idea about dogs was brewing at the back of my mind. When we first moved to The Syke, Little Bear the Lakeland terrier used to accompany me wherever I went, not in a working capacity, as a companion. It is great to have a small dog to hop in and out of the car or Land Rover with you, to walk across the fields checking ponies, and then sit on the settee with you whilst you have a cup of tea. Hector would call this a 'tractor dog', a companion. The collies are great for moving sheep, but with five people living in our house our kitchen is not really big enough to accommodate wet collies.

While the Lakeland terrier is a great, local breed of dog, there were a few issues preventing me from simply buying another. One was that while Little Bear was perfectly happy off lead following me about, Tintin my male terrier had never been able to be let off lead in the twelve years I had had him. He had such a strong hunting instinct and would follow whatever scent he could smell, a rabbit, sheep or alpaca. On rare occasions when visitors had let him out of the garden he was an absolute liability. There was also the issue of the terriers' coats. They were not ideal for walking through mud or wet grass. Baths were a tedious business trying to get the mud out of their coats, and haircuts even worse. Initially I had taken both terriers to a grooming parlour, but at £40 for each dog each month, I had decided to learn to trim them myself. Whilst this saved money it also took up two days every month grooming the dogs.

What I was looking for was a small companion who

would be equally happy outdoors or indoors, able to walk off lead around livestock and not chase any animals, with an easily managed coat. I looked through all the lists of terriers online, but none seemed to quite fit the bill. There seemed to be no guarantee that a terrier could be trusted around livestock.

I turned instead to the pastoral dogs. These could be trusted around livestock if properly trained, and something immediately caught my eye, The Lancashire heeler, and as a bonus is was a breed local to our area. Prior to 1974 and the creation of Cumbria our house was in Lancashire, North of The Sands.

The Lancashire heeler is a small dog developed as a herder and drover of cattle. It is believed to have resulted from breeding a Manchester terrier with a Welsh corgi when corgis were used to drive livestock from Wales to Lancashire and beyond. It has been in existence in Lancashire as a general purpose dog for at least 150 years, although it was only recognised by the Kennel Club as a distinct breed in 1981.

It is classed as a 'vulnerable breed'. In 2007 only 146 Lancashire heelers were registered. This also sparked my interest, why was the breed so little known and why had it fallen out of favour? I began to investigate the history of the Lancashire heeler and found that previously in my area these tiny dogs had been used for herding, moving sheep and cattle and had been a very familiar sight on farms. The coat of the Lancashire heeler is smooth with an undercoat, ideal for getting wet and drying off quickly. They are a small, lively, feisty dog that can work around the farm.

I set about making enquiries and found that there were

actually very few registered breeders. I contacted all the listed breeders on the Kennel Club website. Two replied. One had a boy puppy and one a bitch. I was drawn towards getting another girl, hoping that she would share the kitchen happily with Little Bear, and in a house full of male companions it would be nice to have another female.

I spoke to the breeder with the female puppy on the phone. Here was the first bombshell. The price was £950; equivalent to all the money I had taken for the five Border collie puppies. The second bombshell was that I must sign an agreement to say that I would never breed from her. I had never heard of this before. The puppy was five times the price of a Border collie puppy, and I would have to sign an agreement saying that I would not breed my own replacement companion from her. Could this be why the breed was classed as vulnerable?

Digesting this information I concluded that there was no way that I was going to buy from that breeder. Another route would have to be found. Little Bear had actually been used for breeding prior to me getting her at the age of seven, and my children encouraged me to get another rescue dog.

I found an organisation called the Lancashire Heeler Community. I assumed that this was the breed society, although it subsequently turned out that it was not. I contacted them to say that I was looking for a companion/farm dog, and within a week they had found me one at Buttermere in Cumbria. I arranged to take her on a trial basis, but before I collected her she attacked another dog at that farm so was deemed unsuitable to live with Little Bear.

I had almost given up hope, when about a month later I

was contacted to say that there was a heeler available. She had lived on a farm, and was having to move because she had stolen food out of a child's hand while the child was visiting the farm shop. It subsequently turned out that the previous owner of the farm had moved house and left her. The new owners had not wanted her, so had not fed her. She was relying on hoovering up bits of cattle cake off the floor, so no wonder she was jumping up at children stealing food.

We asked for her to be fully assessed before coming to stay with us on a trial basis. At the assessment centre they said that she would often brush your hand or face with her face, with a protruding canine tooth. You can feel the tooth, but she is not biting. So it turned out, she is quite happy to lick a hand or face but you can feel a tooth bumping against you.

Ruby was approximately seven years old when we collected her. Never one not to let her feelings be known, she communicates through growling. Anything she is unsure of will be growled at. She is defensive of the house and will bark loudly if someone comes to the door. She is not happy if another dog goes near her bed, and I wonder if she has ever had a bed of her own before. The Border collie puppies leave the week that Ruby arrives, and for the few short days that she can watch them playing in the garden she is intrigued with them. One by one they leave to join their families, and Ruby and I look out of the window to see the last puppy leave with her new owners. She looks at me with doleful eyes and gives me a big lick across my face. I can only wonder at what she has seen in her short life.

Apart from being a growly grump, Ruby soon settled in

Ruby, the Lancashire heeler, photograph by Fergus Meanwell.

and formed an immediate bond with me. She loves to squeeze next to me on the settee, or even in bed. At first she was very reluctant to approach anyone else, it takes a long while to earn her trust. She had never had a collar or lead on before, and wet herself the first time she saw my Henry hoover with eyes painted on moving across the floor towards her. Life is not dull with Ruby.

So, how did she get on with the animals? The first week I had her I took her everywhere with me on a lead. The second week I let her off, and not only did she walk alongside me she made an excellent job of checking the lambs.

The last lambs had been born at the beginning of May, and now all the sheep were in an area of rough grazing with their lambs. Ruby and I walked around all the sheep each day. Ruby soon learned to approach the lambs cautiously, making their mothers call them over. We then stood and watched as each lamb was coupled up with its mother and fed. Ruby was actually making the job a lot easier. Having the dog with me made the sheep more protective and spotting the lambs a lot easier. If there were any lambs that did not get up and move for one reason or another (head caught in a fence etc.), Ruby would bark and call me over.

Ruby's tiny stature was also an advantage. Often I could see deer on the horizon, which would have sent the collies into a frenzy, but Ruby was too short to see them and concentrated fully on the sheep.

By the end of the month Ruby could also walk behind sheep to move them with me, and when I clapped my hands to move sheep out of the hay barn Ruby sprang into action and moved them out. She was truly a mini marvel.

Ruby helped us move all the remaining sheep off the hay meadows during May, and the meadows were then 'shut up' to grow hay. We now had a period of very hot, dry weather, and nothing seemed to grow at all. The land became solid, cracked and dusty – most unusual for Cumbria. Instead of an excess of rain we now had difficulty getting water to all the animals, and extra buckets and troughs were put out and refilled on a daily basis. The grass refused to grow. It remained short and covered in sheep poo. This was a rare problem for Cumbria.

Wildfires were reported in the northern Lake District, and appear to be a very real threat throughout Cumbria. The land was bone dry. Holidaymakers coming to our holiday cottage were thrilled with the weather, but we were not so thrilled. We now had another weather crisis to deal with after the appalling wet winter.

The sheep that were feeding lambs did not look well on

the short grass alone and continued to be fed concentrates. All the hay had gone; rarely do you find yourself looking for hay in May, as the grass is normally so abundant. The weather was challenging us from beginning to end this year.

We approached the end of May with sheep and lambs short of grass, and calves about to be born. We hoped and prayed for rain. We were cursing rain in the winter, but now we are desperate for it. Such is life on a hill farm.

At the end of May I took some North Ronaldsay hoggs to a rare breeds auction, hoping to recoup some of the additional money I had spent on feed due to the weather. These hoggs were approximately one year old, and would be suitable for putting to the tup in autumn. I had decided not to increase the numbers of rare breed lambs here because the boy lambs, taken to the auction at five months old and sold 'store' for someone else to fatten on better ground, made one pound each. The cost of the ear tags that they are required to have to go to the auction was one pound each. Instead I have been concentrating on the Ryeland crosses, which made nineteen pounds at a similar age.

I took my excess North Ronaldsay ewes to the rare breed sale. Some have been registered with the Rare Breeds Survival Trust at a cost of £3.60 each plus society membership for the year. I am first into the ring at the auction, dressed smartly, and have prepared a paragraph for the auctioneer to read out which he does:

'North Ronaldsay sheep are the smallest native breed of sheep in the UK. They have featured many times on *Countryfile*, and are excellent conservation grazers. They are ideal for cross-grazing with ponies and will eat weeds.

Their fleeces are highly prized by spinners and the breeder has been selling them for £16 each on eBay. These sheep are registered with the Rare Breeds Survival Trust and are vaccinated, fluked and wormed.'

Try as he might to promote them for me, my first pen of sheep sold for only £10 each. One sheep I particularly liked made £26 sold individually, but all in all it is a dispiriting day. No wonder my sons have refused to come to the rare breed auction with me, selling sheep for £10 each is not the way to raise your social standing in Cumbria.

June

When I think of June, I think of long grass buzzing with pollinators, and happy, tubby sheep and lambs getting fat on the species rich grassland. This year the grass is only just beginning to start to grow. Thankfully the drought ends and it begins to rain. I cannot believe that I have been wishing for rain, after the winter we have had.

A new problem arises – in previous years the sheep have been very happy in their area of rough grazing, but this year with the delayed grass growth they are breaking into our hay meadows and into our neighbour's field.

I get messages on my phone 'Attend to your walling and fencing', but in reality the walls and fences are not in bad repair, the sheep are just hungry due to the lack of grass this year. With the best will in the world, it is pretty much impossible to confine sheep to an area they just don't want to stay in.

They are a crafty lot, my sheep. They know my routine and will be waiting to be fed in the morning in an orderly queue by their hay barn. Later in the evening, when they know I have gone home, they maraud around the Crake Valley like a bunch of hooligans.

I am in the process of buying two more fields so that I can move them about, but in the meantime the serial offenders must be rounded up. There are three main areas where they are escaping.

The first is Tuto Moss, a site of Special Scientific

Interest behind my land. The owner knows my sheep are going in there, and while not wanting them there she doesn't seem to be hopping mad, so we use this escape as a dog training opportunity. Every morning Ruby and I walk across Tuto Moss and then walk the sheep back to our land. Ruby soon gets the hang of this, and calmly walks the sheep back each day. It is only the weekends that are a problem, this area is inaccessible by car and I realise that it is a bit much of me to expect Fergus to shepherd on foot off Tuto Moss each day, so despite not having our Basic Payment Scheme money for 2015 yet (due in December 2015) we decide to put up a new fence.

One hot Saturday, Hector and Fergus replace the fence where it borders Tuto Moss, and I do three wall gaps to placate another neighbour. The bunch of vagabonds cannot then venture onto Tuto Moss, they are successfully contained. The other retrogrades are escaping at the side. Despite me never seeing them there in the mornings, a couple of visits in the evening confirm that they are indeed leaping over walls to escape into my neighbour's ungrazed fields.

These are sheep that have not had lambs, for reasons unknown. I was going to give them another chance to lamb next year as they are large, strong sheep, but this naughtiness seals their fate. They are taken to the auction and make £56 and £44 depending on breed. We get the second best price for 'cast' (older, not suitable for breeding) Rough Fell sheep that week, and I lament that my granddad is not here to pore over the auction report and see our name in print.

The third set of escapees are the most annoying, these are lambs escaping under fences and gates into the hay meadow. You have to admire their tenacity and Ruby's

ability to move them back into the field they are supposed to be in. Drastic measures are called for, and we spend another weekend re-fencing around our hay meadows.

The two new fields are now ours, but we cannot get them fenced and use them immediately due to lack of Basic Payment Scheme funding, and the fact that everybody we could ask to help is very busy at this time of year. The lack of our Basic Payment Scheme Payment is an on-going saga that has been dragging on for months, far too tedious to relate, and we hope that the Rural Payments Agency will be able to calculate our payment soon. They are apparently finding the Cumbrian payments very difficult to process due to common land etc. It is impacting not only on farmers, but businesses that supply farmers which are disappearing at an alarming rate. No farmers in our area appear to have been paid; the payment is now six months later than expected, and nobody has any available money to spend on farm supplies.

This is the first year that I have claimed Basic Payment Scheme funding, and it is not a good introduction. I had not claimed in previous years, as new entrants have to buy entitlements in order to enter the scheme if they do not inherit these entitlements. After six years of farming here I had been able to get the money together to buy the entitlements, at a cost of several thousand pounds, but had yet to see a penny in return for buying into the scheme.

As well as the escaping sheep we are keeping a close eye on the Dexter cattle. During the first week of June my husband and two older boys go to the Dolomites in Italy for a week of running in the mountains. I had hoped that the cows would have calved before they went, but as we wave them off they have not yet shown any signs of calv-

ing. I wave them goodbye on the road outside the house, and walk straight around to the cow field to check on them. One of the cows is lying on her side, pushing – typical, just typical.

I rush inside to tell Fergus to come out quickly as a cow is calving. We stand a safe distance from the cow, about ten metres away on a small hill, and a huge calf slides out of its mum covered in white gunk. I glance at the time on my phone, nine minutes on our own and already we have a new calf. We sit on the hill in the warm sunshine and watch in wonder as the new calf is surrounded by the herd who make gentle reassuring noises while the cow cleans her calf, and he tries to stand for the first time.

No amount of holidays could make up for missing this miracle of nature, as the calf takes his first belly full of milk from his mother who is a first time mum. The bull calf is red, and I call him Rannerdale after a valley near Buttermere that we had recently visited to see the bluebells. In a couple of days he is joined by Primrose, a black heifer calf. Both the mothers are heifers and are first time mums. They both manage the birth and feeding of their calves beautifully without any assistance. This is the advantage of native breeds; I have never had to intervene with the delivery of a calf or help a calf in any way. We manage to coax both Rannerdale and Primrose into the handling area and ear tag them safely.

The remaining cows will calve in August due to them not being pregnant when tested by the vet after a visit to a neighbour's bull. It is believed that the bull suffered from a raised temperature after having a sheep tick, and was therefore temporarily infertile after the first two weeks of their visit. The cows were then artificially inseminated, as we did not have access to another pedigree bull locally.

Spurred on by our success with our cast sheep, we sort some more out to sell. Two rare breed sheep and three Rough Fells. The Rough Fells were not good mothers and had to have help feeding their lambs. They are taken to the auction, as having sheep with good mothering abilities is crucial to the success of the flock in the long run. Sometimes you have to make hard decisions about your flock going forward, however pretty the sheep may be, you want a flock with excellent health status and good mothering instincts. Similarly, any sheep with persistent foot problems are not used for breeding. The last thing you want as a shepherd is a flock with foot problems that require regular attention and treating.

The two rare breed sheep make the obligatory one pound each, but something goes drastically wrong with the Rough Fells, and instead of making about £50 each these large, fit sheep make £5each. After auction commission, my cheque for five sheep comes to £9.

On the day I receive this cheque I also get a message from a local restaurant asking if I have any mutton available for a dish they are trialling. Sometimes things do not go your way, but I resolve to be a lot smarter when selling sheep in the future. I cannot believe that my large sheep made only £5 each. In future I will have to stay with the sheep, and bring them home if they do not get a reasonable bid. Working for nothing, for the joy of it and covering your costs is one thing, working for a loss is unacceptable.

During June my eldest son Oscar finishes university in Edinburgh for the summer and returns home with a friend from Holland. The friend is interested in all that we do, having grown up on a dairy farm that now has no animals and has been converted to holiday accommodation. He is fascinated by the idea of hefting and common land. We go to watch Oscar run in a fell race at Broughton Mills, which he wins, and we stand on the fell tops looking across to the Irish sea in one direction and the Lake District fells to the other. It is indeed a fine place to live and we enjoy showing it to a visitor.

Visitors at The Syke are infrequent due to us having a large family with no spare bedroom, and always being busy. I appreciate that it can also appear a little odd to some visitors that we have little time to spend indoors as we are generally outside while there is daylight. It is quite refreshing to have a guest, and to explain our lifestyle to him.

At the end of June there is thankfully more grass beginning to grow in the meadow. Three years without adding fertiliser have also allowed more wildflowers to grow and I spot meadow vetchling, self heal and betony growing where previously there had been only grass. It is my belief that grass mixed with flowers will provide a more varied diet and better nutrition in winter for the sheep, although to re-seed the meadow completely with a mix of the parasitic plant yellow rattle would not have provided enough crop to feed the sheep during winter, which is the primary purpose of the meadow as well as supporting wildlife.

Thankfully my plan seems to be working, and wildflower seeds that have lain dormant in the soil are now re-establishing themselves and more pollinators can be seen buzzing about the meadow.

It must be noted that there is something of a generational

divide here. Hector who is at agricultural college is not at all impressed with the plan. He thinks that we should fertilise in order to encourage more grass growth that would create more bales of hay and would therefore be worth more money. As I keep telling him, if it was all about making money I would go and work somewhere like a bank for a wage.

It is more important to do your bit for the environment for the future, as well as building up a quality flock and herd. It is not about money, which is just as well really as if it was the project would have been written off as a failure by now. As it is we are making small steps towards a sustainable farm, along the lines of the old saying 'live for today, farm for tomorrow'. I appreciate that the younger generation aspire to make large strides and not small steps, and in order to achieve this they may have to stride off into the sunset at some point.

Our small farm will not be able to keep up with their aspirations. The thirst for travel and new experiences can often leave you with an appreciation of what you had in the first place, and a lament for what has been lost if someone has not been keeping it ticking over in the meantime. I will be here, making the small steps as long as I am physically able if the boys want to travel and explore the world. If the boys genuinely want to stay and work together, another solution may have to be found in order to meet everybody's aspirations. Time will tell.

July

At the beginning of July, on Fergus' thirteenth birthday, there is great excitement as the BBC *Antiques Roadshow* has come to a large stately home near where we live. Banners appear on the roadside advertising the event. I ask my son what he wants to do on his birthday, as his school term has finished at the end of June, and he replies, 'Go to the *Antiques Roadshow* and get on TV.'

We decide to take some farm related antiques for a valuation, as the banners say that they are looking for antiques with a story behind them. We take a 1934 Rough Fell Sheep flock book and a *Shepherds Guide to the Lake District*, with their 2015 equivalents for comparison. I take a toy farm that was made by my great granddad for my granddad in the 1920s.

Our enthusiasm for 'getting on the TV' wanes somewhat when we have spent two hours queuing in the rain to get in. As soon as my son presents his books at the information desk, with a long explanation of smit marks, hefting, and what makes a good ewe in his opinion, the lady behind the desk calls for the producer and we are no longer queuing in the rain, in fact we are in a hospitality area eating a BBC lunch with the presenter of the programme Fiona Bruce, and some of the antiques experts.

They would like us to film a 'quickie', a short piece about flock books and shepherds' guides in between the valuable items such as some first edition Beatrix Potter books. My toy farm has been forgotten about, but whilst we are waiting one of the experts asks me what is in the bag. He loves the farm and values it at £300, not that we would ever sell it. My granddad never got a real farm, and the toy farm standing at the top of the stairs reminds me every night how lucky I am as I go up to bed.

My son records his 'piece to camera' and it goes well. He talks about his uncle's smit mark and shows the expert his name in the shepherd's guide. We now have to wait until the show is broadcast to see if it makes the final cut.

We have another day out following the *Antiques Roadshow* when we go to the Great Yorkshire Show as a friend of ours is showing sheep there and offers us a free ticket. It is our first agricultural show of the year and is oppressively hot; summer has arrived. We meander around the show marvelling at the vast array of agricultural machinery that we will never be able to afford. The boys enjoy looking at huge tractors and get a whole variety of freebies. We do not give out our address, as last year we were visited at home by an agricultural rep who said that my son had agreed to buy a silage pit cover at a show. She stood outside the house, looked about and said, 'I can't see a silage pit anywhere'. Rather embarrassing! We get lots of cups of tea and biscuits, and buy some dog food and clothing – a grand day out.

During July we get the news that we have been hoping for, that our valley is not the preferred site for the Lynx UK Trust release of lynx as part of a rewilding project. Our valley had been in the short list of five suggested sites. Despite the trust's assertion that a lynx would only eat 0.4 sheep/year and that we would be fully compensated for any losses, I would probably have felt it was safer to stop keeping my Ouessant sheep here, as they would be such easy pickings for a lynx. To contain them in a small lynx proof area would also be unfair to them, depriving them of their freedom.

The trust does not deny that the lynx would eat sheep, and seem to think that it would be acceptable to compensate us financially for any losses. What the organisation does not understand is that a sheep is not merely a commodity. Hefted sheep have to be taught their heft by their mother. Sheep in our area need to be resistant to ticks that the red deer carry. It is very difficult and unfair to the sheep to buy in animals from another area and expect them to survive here. I do not believe that it is acceptable to release a predatory large cat into my tiny sheep's habitat. It seems incredible that an organisation could release a lynx that would hunt on our land, land that we have specifically bought for the purposes of breeding pedigree sheep. There seems to be an assumption that land in a national park is 'for the nation', for the consensus of public opinion, when a lot of it is privately owned.

The BBC *Farming Today* programme record an interview with my views on rewilding and the lynx introduction, and I spend a lot of time responding to pro-lynx comments on Twitter. I imagine these people to be 'armchair rewilders' who have no experience of managing a landscape but think the lynx would be a nice idea. I may be doing them a disservice.

Cumbria Wildlife Trust is not in favour of my valley as a suitable site for the lynx. They prefer to manage landscapes with farmers rather than impose such schemes upon them. An incident happens which despite being tragic, and I would be devastated if it was my sheep, does our position as sheep farmers a huge favour. This is when a lynx escapes from a zoo in Dartmoor and is at large for three weeks while various experts try to recapture it. We don't know how many animals it ate during those three weeks, but it is eventually caught when it kills four lambs in one day and gives away its location by their carcases. So much for 0.4 sheep per year, this one ate four in a day. I suspect that in the future we may be very grateful to it for doing that. Good old Flavio, which was the rather unlikely name of the escaped lynx.

Much of my daily life and annual routine would have been recognisable to those farming in our valley in the sixteenth century, but responding to tweets and recording radio interviews are what the twenty-first century shepherdess has to do in order to get our voice heard amongst other, often more educated, voices. Very few farmers in my area have the desire or confidence to interact with the general public, and I feel that somebody must speak out or our views will not be heard.

The sheep farmer's voice is represented by the National Sheep Association, who published an excellent paper on the value of sheep in the uplands. They also refused to join the panel of experts advising the Lynx UK Trust about the introduction of the lynx, as they are totally opposed to it. These initiatives are excellent, but often we seem to be speaking to ourselves, preaching to the converted, when it is perhaps the newspaper readers lying in bed browsing rewilding articles on their iPads and thinking that rewilding sounds like an excellent idea that we need to engage with.

Hopefully some of these people will follow me on Twitter and see the work we do for wildlife and our environment here, and consider shepherding a worthwhile profession.

Stepping back into the shepherding that our ancestors would recognise, I begin shearing. We have a shearer booked to come at the end of the month to shear the larger Rough Fell sheep, but I will attempt to shear all the smaller rare breeds with hand shears before then.

The Ouessant sheep are easily caught, and so on the first day of my shearing marathon I shear them. I have new shears, which take a bit of getting used to, but manage on my own to catch, shear and roll the fleeces. After shearing, each sheep then has a mini health check, a pedicure, wormer and fly/tick treatment. Their udders are checked again.

I then set myself the target of shearing four sheep per day. I entice them into a building or pen, by rattling a bucket of food, and catch them. It is better to hand shear the rare breeds if possible, as hand spinners prefer that. I photograph some of the fleeces, put the pictures on Twitter, and sell them for ten pounds each. The rest will be stored and sold on eBay.

I shear the Shetlands in five days, and move on to the Hebrideans and North Ronaldsays. I am up to speed now, and spend an hour a day shearing nine sheep. The sheep that have never been sheared before try to escape my grasp, but those that have previously been sheared do not wriggle and are very happy to lose their fleece. Sheep obviously have good memories; they can remember being sheared last year and are not afraid.

Sheep are often depicted as being without an opinion

blindly following each other. In fact they inhabit a complex matriarchal society, in which the older sheep teach the younger sheep through example. They are quick learners, crafty at out-witting human attempts to contain them. There is much to admire about how sheep live their lives peacefully alongside each other in a structured society respectful of age. Not too long ago a team of British scientists has shown that sheep are able to recognize the individual faces of at least 50 sheep and remember them for more than two years – they can also remember individual humans too.

When shearing a sheep I sit her on her bottom, with all four legs off the ground. Her head flops loosely and she relaxes if she has been sheared before. Sometimes I tuck their head between my legs. I make a small cut through the fleece at the neck in order to make a way into the fleece, then push the fleece back gently with my hand. It is important not to pull the fleece too hard or the skin may rise up and get nicked by the shears.

I cut one way down the side of the fleece, and keep making long cuts down the back of the sheep working from one side to another. The only problem comes if the sheep is larger than my arms are long, and then sometimes the sheep is left with a pompom on her bottom! I have to cut that off when she stands up. The fleece is very stretchy in the summer, the good weather makes it 'rise' away from the skin and it is easy to cut it off. Left alone and not sheared the fleece would eventually be rubbed off to be replaced by a new fleece for winter.

All that remain to shear are the Ryelands. They are notoriously difficult to shear with their woolly tummies. After I have sheared these, and the shearer is delayed due to hay

making commitments at home and shear sharpening issues, I tackle the Rough Fell hoggs. These are on the very limit of what I can physically manage alone, and jittery because they have never been sheared before. There is a spot on their bottom that I just cannot reach, and if I don't get it snipped off as they stand up they are left with pompom bottoms – not a good look.

We get the news that the shearer is coming the next day, and set off early to gather the sheep from their area of rough grazing. Ruby has not experienced this yet, and it is a day where there's no time for anything to go wrong, so the collies are called into action.

The boys wait near the building while I go off to gather in the sheep. There is no rush, no panic. The sheep have to feel happy and calm when they come in. I simply shout for my oldest sheep and they come running. I walk in front of them shouting 'Come on girls' and they follow me. I walk over to the building with them all around me, and rattle a few feed bags. They rush into the building to see what is going on, and we confine them in approximately a third of the building with hurdles locked together to make a barrier. These sheep then realise that they have forgotten their lambs in the rush. We open the doors into the second third of the building, and retreat to a safe distance. The sheep then call their lambs, and they come running. We have to be patient, and wait until all the lambs are in before we shut the gates. The lambs are then reunited with their mothers and everyone is happy.

The boys retreat to a hill behind the building, and I go and get the ewes in an area about half a mile in front of them. I take Moss with me, and we walk around the sheep, gathering them into a group. Once we have a group of about twenty I attempt to walk them back. After a couple of hesitant starts, my son's black Shetland ewe takes charge. She knows where she is going, and leads all the sheep. I follow behind with Moss, encouraging the lambs to follow on. The boys see the sheep coming through the fields, and move forward to block the route behind the building.

'It's OK' I shout as loud as I can. 'The black Shetland is leading them. Stay back out of sight.' The Shetland leads on, taking them into the building following well trodden sheep trods and taking the driest route. Patiently we wait for the sheep to come around the final hill and into the building; again we feed them and then secure them with hurdles. Moss and I encourage the lambs to join them.

So far so good, it is still very early in the morning and

we have two thirds of our sheep in. I then set off to 'sweep' the remaining gorse bushes and rushes, gathering a group of sheep in front of Moss and myself. These take a little more persuading and do about five laps of the building before we can encourage them to go in. We are just left with one sheep and one lamb under a tree about half a mile away. I set off and discover four more sheep en route, and bring the remaining five sheep back.

We can now breathe a sigh of relief. The sheep are in the building, which is half of our work done. We lie on the grass and get out flasks of tea and pasties. While we are eating it begins to drizzle and we are all glad that we got up early. If the sheep are wet they cannot be sheared.

One of the boys dashes off to a hilltop to try and find some mobile signal to phone the shearer and tell him that we still want him to come and shear because the sheep are dry. The reality is that the sheep must now be sheared today, one way or another, and we do not want to hand shear them all.

My son sends a message but will not be able to receive a reply, and we hope that the shearer will come and begin to sort out the lambs. The lambs are all put together in some hurdles and we have a good look at them. A lot of time is spent observing and considering sheep if you are a shepherd. Two tup lambs are considered show worthy, so these are taken home. They will be weaned, or 'spained' as we would say, from their mothers and taught to stand nicely at a show. They will also be fed and handled every morning so that they become used to us. We all agree that we like one tup lamb, and hopefully we will be able to sell him as a tup in the future. The second one's fate is undecided. Only the best one per cent of male sheep will become tups as quality breeding demands only the very best.

The remaining lambs are marked red on their heads for female flock replacements, and have purple flock marks put on them. They are all wormed and treated for fly and tick prevention. Any lambs left unmarked are for selling for meat, at a date to be decided. It is part of being a farmer that you accept that this will happen. These lambs will be looked after as well as we can, but none will be given names now.

The lambs are released from the building, leaving their mothers inside. The adult sheep I have already sheared are given new markings, flock marks for all, and released. The remaining ewes are in the building waiting, and we come to the grim realisation that we will have to begin hand shearing. I have run out of the tick preventative treatment, so nip off to the shop and am very pleased on my return twenty minutes later to see a familiar tractor parked in the field.

The electric shearing machine is set up, powered from the Land Rover battery, and we all get into position to begin shearing. I am to catch the sheep and pass them to one of the two shearers. Hector will shear with hand shears and his friend with electric shears, then the sheep will be passed back to me to mark, treat for flies and ticks, worm them and then put them outside the building. Fergus will roll the fleeces and put them into the Wool Board bag that he has strung between two old gates in anticipation. It is a huge bag that he physically climbs into to compress the fleeces. It needs to be absolutely full to capacity as we are charged for each bag that is picked up by the wool board haulier.

All the Rough Fell fleeces will be sent to the Wool Board for them to auction off. They are not suitable for hand spinning and will be used for carpet production or something similar. Last year I received £37 for them from the Wool Board. 'Is that each?' someone asked on Twitter. Sadly not, it was for the whole lot once the cost of collecting the bags and transporting them to the depot had been deducted.

We work hard all afternoon in the heat, all four of us. There are shouts as sheep wriggle, and the constant buzz of the shears. Bottles of water are drunk. Regularly we pause and look at how many we have to go, before setting off again. Everybody likes a chance to straighten his or her back and have a quick chat. It is hard work, but companionable, almost a social occasion. Shearing relies on teamwork, and we all get along happily. Nobody gets stressed, nobody gets mad with the sheep or each other. The odd sheep gets nicked by the shears and treated with an iodine spray, but no sheep are injured, kicked or mistreated. I feel that I must point this out as sheep shearers have had such a bad press recently, with animal welfare groups saying that sheep are mistreated during shearing. That is the last thing I would expect to see in the Lake District. Sheep are treated with respect and dignity: we love our sheep.

At the end of the afternoon the last sheep is released from the building and goes off purposefully to find her lambs. We tidy up the building that is littered with loose bits of wool on the floor. The floor of the building is then covered in pallets, as all being well the shed will be full of hay by the end of the week. The forecast is good, the grass growth is just about acceptable, and it is time to make hay.

The grass growth has been monitored by Hector, and by our neighbours, and I have watched the plants flower and set their seed. The long range weather forecast is for rain; so now is the optimum time to make hay. The whole process will take three days, during which it must not rain or the grass will be spoiled. This would not be the end of the crop, as it would have been for our ancestors, as there is still the possibility of making silage for the cows to eat. We had to do this two years ago, and buy in hay for the sheep, so I am anxious about the whole process.

The grass is cut, and then spun twice to dry it out. It is then rowed up and baled. Our neighbours do this for us, and we are only needed to help on baling day. We have had to widen the gates of the hay meadow in order to accommodate my neighbour's big tractor.

On baling day my job is usually to move the bales into eights, so that they can be picked up by a grab. It is hot, hard work. You need protective gloves on or the strings will tear your hands to ribbons. Thankfully the weather holds and we can make hay. Due to the lack of rain this summer we have about 50 fewer bales this year than last from the same area of land, which may cause us problems in the winter.

We will not think of that now, for now the hay is safely in the shed, the sheep are sheared, and we can breathe and sleep easy once more; or we could sleep easy if it were not for some imminent arrivals. Another of our Border collies is expecting litter of puppies, and I check her during the night. She has been moved into her own 'loose box', a large stable, and is making herself at home moving towels and shavings in and out of the whelping box.

She delivers nine puppies early one morning. One is very tiny, the size of a dormouse, and does not take a breath. She watches me with doleful eyes as I take this puppy away and my heart breaks for her. Funny to think that in eight weeks time she will be ready to say goodbye to these babies. There are five boys and three girls. One of the girls is very tiny but we make sure that she feeds regularly and she grows slowly but surely. We weigh and check on her every couple of hours, and we all will her to live. We hope that in eight weeks time we will be waving her off to a new home, time will tell.

August

August is a time for holidays, a time when the Lake District is inundated with visitors enjoying the lakes, fells and coffee shops. Recently we have not had good weather in August, getting our best weather in May and September. August is often a wet month, but for us August is a month of agricultural shows.

Agricultural shows are the shepherding equivalent of a holiday when we join our fellow shepherds in showing sheep, socialising and relaxing away from the farm. It is a big effort to get sheep ready for a show. Sheep must be chosen from the flock, well handled, groomed and kept in an accessible place. We have a small field which is a DEFRA approved isolation area, and the sheep can go to shows moving in and out of the isolation area without having to observe the usual standstill rules. Sheep at a show must obviously be in good health, and sheep have a remarkable ability to appear well all year, only to suddenly limp or scour (get diarrhoea) immediately before a show.

The prize money on offer for winning a show, perhaps £20 at best and £3 at a local show, does not represent the pride in having a prize winning sheep which in turn reflects well on the flock. It is a source of great pride to show sheep, it is not about money and more about recognition from the farming community. The rosettes pinned to the beams of your farmhouse might just help you get through the harshest of winters, dreaming of show successes in the summer.

It is not easy to win at showing sheep, as the competition is intense. Each local breed usually has its own set of classes to enter, depending on the sheep's gender, age, the age of breeder, size of flock, etc. Below is an example of the different classes that Rough Fell Sheep can be entered into at a local show:

- Aged ram
- Shearling ram
- Ram lamb in the hands of the breeder
- Ewe which has reared a lamb in the current year
- Shearling gimmer
- Gimmer lamb in the hands of the breeder
- Ram lamb entered and shown by young farmer aged sixteen or under
- Gimmer lamb entered and shown by young farmer aged sixteen or under
- Best starred ram
- Champion young handler
- Best two females and one male in the hands of the breeder

At larger shows there will also be classes for small and large breeders. This year in addition to our two local shows (Hawkshead and Lowick) and the Westmorland County Show at the beginning of September, my uncle has asked us to take our sheep and dogs to his local show, the Ravenstonedale Show, on 20 August. He is president of the show this year, and would like his family to share the day with him. Unfortunately it is the same day as the Rusland Show, a horticultural show, which we will have to miss. My eldest son Oscar is determined to try and get the fell race record at the 126th show in 2016, so we will be sorry to miss it.

Early in August we begin to collect our show team into an accessible area. I will be showing my Ouessants, my Ryeland tups, Rough Fells of various ages and two Welsh Hill Speckle Faced sheep that I have been given by the breed society to show in Cumbria and promote their breed – like an advertisement – so the pressure is on to do well. In some classes we all agree which are the best sheep, in others we disagree so there is a lot of discussion and debate.

We have the time and space to ponder the suitability of the sheep for showing as our daily routine is easier in midsummer. The only sheep to be fed are the show sheep, the others are 'away at grass', at large in areas of rough grazing, enjoying their freedom and the summer grasses. We walk around all of the animals daily, but there is no responsibility to keep them fed. As we wander, we ponder, and dream of rosettes.

As the show weekend approaches we begin watching the weather forecast with alarm. A very wet day is forecast. A wet show is always a shame, as there are fewer visitors to the show and you don't feel like standing around and socialising in the rain. The week before the show the boys spend most of their evenings round at the Rusland Show field putting up marquees. Everybody is talking about the weather forecast for the weekend.

On show day my alarm goes off at 5.30am and I get out of bed and walk the dogs. Some of the dogs are coming to the show and some are staying at home, but they all get a walk and their breakfast as it is going to be a long day for everybody. At 6.30 I have my breakfast and go to wake up the boys, and we go to gather the sheep. We used to put the sheep in a building the night before the show but they had a habit of rubbing on walls and getting grubby.

This morning the sheep sense that something different is happening and do not want to come over when I attempt to gather them in just by shouting. Normally they will come running into the pens in anticipation of getting food, but today they stand and stare, so we go and get the dogs to get them in. As soon as the sheep see the dogs approaching they decide to do the sensible thing and come into the sheep pens. We then have to pick out the ones we want and put them into the trailer. One appears to have developed a limp overnight and is put back into the field.

We are soon travelling along the M6 motorway, but the weather is atrocious. When the motorway cuts through the Howgill Fells at Tebay it feels as if we are in a wind tunnel being buffeted about. I can feel the sheep trailer being blown around. It is a nervous drive, and we all sit in silence.

We arrive at the show field with about fifteen minutes to go until the sheep judging starts. We are now in a state of mild panic. The sheep have obviously not had a good journey. It looks as though they have been climbing on each other. They have mud on their faces and mud on their backs.

We have brought flasks of warm water, horse brushes and fairy liquid with us to wash the sheep on arrival. Fergus is so distressed with the appearance of his gimmer lambs that he tips a whole bucket of water over them. This has the effect of totally saturating the fleeces, and making the sheep look about half the size that they did when we arrived. We are all storming about in a terrible mood.

All our sheep have been put in one pen and I have to move the tiny Ouessant sheep out of the Rough Fell section and into 'Any Other Breed'. I begin to walk them down one of the alleys made of hurdles, when somebody goes out at the other end and leaves the gate open. The gate is straight onto Orton Fell, thousands of acres of unfenced grazing. 'Stop those sheep' I shout, but nobody hears me. 'Help, somebody stop those sheep,' I shout. I am literally screaming at the top of my voice now. For some reason the sheep stop by themselves, and I am able to run ahead of them and slam the gate. It is pouring with rain, which is just as well, as I am so soaked that nobody notices that I have tears running down my face. Fergus comes over and says 'Mother you were literally screeching. Please stop showing us up!'

Needless to say showing the sheep is not a success and my Ouessants are not appreciated. In the 'Any Other Breed' section there are nine Zwartbles and my Ouessants. The judge moves down the line feeling the fat on the back of each Zwartble, and he does the same to my Ouessant each time. I want to tell him that it is not about fat, it is about fleece, attitude, poise and a hundred other things, but there is no time for conversation. My tiny sheep are passed over.

The Welsh Hill sheep gets a third, and I am relieved that I will not be going home empty handed. At one point the Ouessants manage to escape their pen again, and get out into the alley. A man picks one up in each hand, by the fleece on their backs, and plonks them into their pen. I can see that it was not a wise idea bringing them here.

Over at the Rough Fell pens my sons are still waiting. The adult breeders show their sheep first here, then the young people. There is a break for lunch and a terrific downpour, and we all go and sit in the Land Rover and eat our sandwiches. After lunch the boys get to show their Rough Fells with the other breeders who are under eighteen. They get a second and two thirds, but we can all see that our sheep don't look as good as the other breeders here. They look very bedraggled after the long trailer ride here.

It is then time for the dog show. By now a lot of the planned activities such as the brass band competition have had to be cancelled. It is such a shame. My uncle, the president, makes his way across the field to judge the dog show. In all the years he has visited Ravenstonedale Show since he was a child he has never seen such a wet show day in his life. Most of the visitors are long gone. Ruby is the only small dog still on the show field to enter the dog show.

When you think of shows you are going to go to you imagine yourself showing sheep in the sun, chatting to friends and relations. This show is a total washout. In response to the weather we are allowed to take our sheep home early, normally we would have to wait until 4pm.

We are soon heading back down the motorway, but the weather is getting worse. The Land Rover is hard to keep on track as it is so windy, and a huge metal motorway sign blows across the road in front of us just missing the front of the vehicle.

We realise that we might be able to make it back in time for the Rusland Show, and keep driving on despite the weather. The fastest speed we reach on the motorway is 40mph. It is just not safe enough to go any faster. Once at Rusland we pop the sheep into our building with some hay, and go straight round to the Rusland Show.

Rusland Show would normally be in full swing, but there are just a handful of people on the field, some of the show committee finishing off a barrel of beer in the beer tent. They explain that due to safety concerns, the genuine worry that a marquee might blow down, the show has been abandoned. Later we see on the news that on Orkney a field of marquees has been blown into the sea.

Usually the marquees are moved straight from the Rusland Show to the Hawkshead Show on Tuesday. We are hoping to show sheep there, but we get an email to say that the show has been cancelled due to a waterlogged field. The show day itself turns out to be a beautifully sunny day, but the field is still too wet to allow vehicles on to; what a disastrous summer.

We have been anxiously watching our Dexter Cattle while all the show preparations have been underway, but there is still no sign of them calving. These are the cows that did not get pregnant from the bull so were artificially inseminated. My neighbour phones to say that all of his cows that were artificially inseminated at the same time have all finished calving, and asks how we are getting on. I tell him they are showing no signs of calving, and 20 minutes later we have them in the handling area and he comes round with plastic gloves and lubricant to pregnancy test them. They are not pregnant. It's a depressing day as we realise that these cows will probably have to be fattened and sold as meat now rather than kept as breeding cows.

We have been looking for a larger farm that can provide employment for Hector when he leaves college as well as myself for some time. We were asked by the Prince's Trust in April if we were interested in a farm in Northumberland

and towards the end of August we receive the letting details.

The farm is a large sheep farm in the Coquet Valley owned by the Ministry of Defence. There is also a tea room, holiday let and bunkbarn with campsite. The incoming tenant will have to buy the outgoing tenant's 900 sheep.

A very sunny day at the end of August sees us driving up the Coquet Valley for the first time. The red flags are flying showing that the army are using the land for manoeuvres, but there are still plenty of visitors enjoying the sunshine, swimming in the river and visiting the tearooms. One of the main features of the farm are the spectacular hay meadows that are classified as Sites of Special Scientific Interest. There is a modern farmhouse that also houses the tearoom, and a very old farmhouse that has been unoccupied since 1969.

We love the farm, particularly liking the nature of the fell (easy to gather) and the old farmhouse. A plan comes to mind whereby we would renovate the old farmhouse and use the new farmhouse for bed and breakfast guests. The application has to include a 5-year financial plan for the farm, and is submitted with a tender for the rent to the agent. We will hear in September if we have an interview, and if we are lucky enough to be offered the tenancy we will have to move in on 14 November. It is a frightening thought, but the decision is now out of our hands and all we can do is wait.

September

We have two shows during the first week of September, and our hopes are for hot, dry days after the washout that was August. The first show is the Lowick Show, which is our local show in the Crake Valley and always on the first Saturday in September. The show is called the Lowick 'L'al Royal' Show, and has been held here for over 150 years, but nobody I have asked seems to know why it is called the L'al Royal.

At the Lowick Show there are classes for a whole variety of sheep. We have entered the horned sheep category, which is for Rough Fells, Swaledales and Scottish Black-faces, and native and rare breed sheep for our Welsh Hill Speckle Faced sheep, our Ryeland and North Ronaldsay tups.

The weather forecast is not looking good for the show, and we have waterproofs and changes of clothing packed. Yet again, show day dawns with torrential rain. Cars are being pulled on to the car park field and the rain is absolutely pouring down when we arrive.

There are not as many people as usual showing horned sheep, perhaps because of the weather, and we win champion horned sheep, and best horned sheep in the show area, with one of our shearlings. There are trophies for both, but because of the torrential rain there is no prize giving today and sheep can be taken home early. We collect our trophies and load up the Land Rover and trailer with our bedraggled sheep and dogs. It is very dispiriting, we imagined sitting in the sun eating a picnic, but by lunchtime we are already heading home. We have more rosettes and trophies than we could have dreamed of, but it is disappointing that the show has had to be called off early.

I look at the names engraved on the best horned sheep trophy, and see one of my neighbours named as winning in 1978, '79, '80, '82 and '84. Our neighbours are celebrating their diamond-wedding anniversary this week. They were married in the church around the corner, and for their wedding anniversary everyone is invited to an afternoon of tea and cake at the Rusland Reading Rooms opposite the church.

My neighbour is one of the most fascinating people I know. He is a walking encyclopaedia of sheep information. In a short conversation with him recently he told me about going to Scotland on the train to buy Cheviot sheep, bringing them home on the train, and walking them through Ulverston town. On another occasion he told me about walking sheep home through Hawkshead village, in the midst of all the traffic before the bypass was built.

When he was a young man, his interests were breeding sheep, fell running and visiting country shows. Nothing much has changed in this valley, my boys still have the same interests today.

The climax of the showing season is the Westmorland Show, which is our local county show. It is held on the first Thursday in September near Kendal, and attracts crowds of around 25,000 people. Our entries for the show have been put in several weeks in advance, and a day off school has been approved for my son. This year we also have anxiety about not only which sheep to take, but whether our Land Rover will be fixed for the show. On the way home from the Lowick Show, with all of our show sheep in the trailer, the prop shaft broke and the Land Rover ground to a halt in the middle of the road.

Hector jumped out and walked off to find help, leaving me with an abandoned car and trailer blocking the road. After about half an hour he returned with a neighbour – people will always find time to help each other out, and the total lack of mobile phone signal in the valley means that you have no hope of phoning for a breakdown truck anyway.

Our neighbour towed the Land Rover home, and I was left blocking the road with just the abandoned sheep trailer. There is very little traffic on our lanes, but some bemused tourists appeared from nowhere and sat puzzling out why I would be stood in the torrential rain next to a trailer full of sheep blocking the road.

Another neighbour drove up and informed me that the Land Rover was nearly at home, travelling very slowly at about 5mph, and not to worry someone would be along for me shortly. The man who repairs our Land Rover lives in the next village and as soon as I got home I phoned him and explain the urgency around getting the sheep to the Westmorland Show in five days time. He came over immediately to collect the broken parts of the prop shaft in order to make some replacements, and on the evening before the show the Land Rover is judged fit to drive again.

Yet again the weather forecast looks terrible and we fill the back of the Land Rover with waterproofs and flasks of tea. I get up at 5.30am on the morning of the show to assess the situation with the sheep and double check on who will be going.

The sheep cunningly sense that something is going on because I am up so early, so I go back home and get the Border collies to contain them in a pen made at the end of the isolation area. At this point I am trying to control my rising anxiety that the sheep will do something stupid like jump over the walls. I take deep breaths to slow my heart rate down. Animals are very perceptive about a person's state of mind. There is no way that any sheep will want to go into a pen with an anxious farmer.

Around 6am Hector appears and between the two of us and three dogs we manage to contain the sheep. I have entered both of my Welsh Hill Speckle Faced shearlings, but one has developed a slight limp. Hector vetoes me taking her. He states it is bad for business to be seen with a limping sheep, and we load the rest of the sheep into the trailer, take off our waterproofs for the journey and set off.

When we get to the show field there is a break in the rain. Hector says he will park the Land Rover and trailer if I pen the sheep. I jump out with the sheep, there is a queue of trailers behind and there is no time to grab my waterproofs.

The sheep need to go into three different areas of pens. Most people will just have one breed of sheep and their sheep can be easily directed into the pen. My Rough Fell and North Ronaldsay sheep get penned easily, and I attempt to walk the Welsh Hill Speckle Faced sheep to its area over the other side of the pens. One sheep is very hard to control on her own, she is a flock animal, and she starts to panic. At this moment the heavens open with the most torrential rain storm I have ever known in my life. I stand in my shirt-sleeves and jeans, soaked absolutely to the skin, and watch my sheep vault the pens and run off into the stalls that are set up selling agricultural equipment.

I am drenched, I can feel the mascara running down my cheeks, my hair is hanging in dripping rats' tails, and my best sheep is currently loose amongst dozens of stalls. It is not yet 8am. What else can possibly go wrong?

Sometimes you have to laugh. I slip and slide in the mud as I run around the stalls laughing and chasing my sheep. Suddenly she stops, looks round, and takes stock of the situation; she is the only sheep in sight; she bleats, and nobody replies. Sheep are herd animals and do not like to be alone. I can see her thinking about what to do next, then suddenly she belts past me at a fantastic speed, heading back towards the sheep pens. I follow, flapping my arms and shouting, 'Open that sheep pen' to whoever is within earshot. Thankfully somebody realises what is happening and opens the pen, and my sheep runs in. I bend over with my hands on my knees, totally exhausted from the exertion of it all, and lift my face up to the sky as the rain washes the last traces of make up away.

It is near impossible to warm up and get dry again if you are outdoors and this wet. I put on waterproofs over my clothes, but am very cold. The sheep judging is due to start at 9.30am. Fergus is with his North Ronaldsay sheep in his section, Hector is with the Rough Fells, ready to call Fergus over if his sheep need to be shown there, and I am on my own in the any other breed section.

It is to be hoped that the judge of any other breed will have read up on the breed standards of the sheep entered in the class today. I know that mine is an excellent sheep, having been given to me by the Welsh Hill Speckle Faced Sheep Society to show in Cumbria and try to promote the breed. I know she meets all the breed standards and am very optimistic about her chances of winning.

Strangely the judge has not arrived by 10.00am, but we keep waiting in the pens in the rain. I am anxious to know how Fergus and Hector are getting on, but daren't leave my section in case the judge arrives. We wait, patiently, in the torrential rain until midday, and still nobody has arrived to judge the sheep. Various people have come and reassured us that they know that we are waiting for a judge, but the judge does not arrive. The Rough Fell and North Ronaldsay sheep have been judged by now, and the rest of the breeds are ready to start the interbreed championship. There is not a champion sheep from our section to go forward, so it is decided that someone else must be found to judge our sheep.

A replacement judge is found. He has never heard of the breed of sheep that I am holding. How then, can he judge it against the breed standards? My heart sinks, it is not going to be our day. I get fifth place, and a rosette, that is something at least.

Fergus has done quite well with his sheep, third and fourth places, but no winning red rosette like last year. There is a general feeling that this is not our day, whereas last year at this time we felt on top of the world after winning our class. He decides not to bother entering the young handlers competition, as he is thoroughly soaked. We all retire to the Land Rover and eat our sandwiches in soggy silence.

Will these wet days put us off showing our sheep? Not at all. Next year we will be trying again. Everybody has an off day, and this was ours. We make the most of the hospitality that the NFU, auction, feed suppliers, etc. have to offer by enjoying lots of free cups of tea and cakes until it is time to go home. We are all relieved to get home and unload the trailer. Showing is over for another year, and what a torrential time it has been.

In mid-September it is time to say goodbye to the latest litter of puppies. These have all been reserved after advertising them on the internet, and the puppies are taken to be microchipped at the vets with the details of their new owners. The tiny girl puppy is still smaller than the others, but has found a home with a lady who has recently lost her Border collie. I am not overly keen on letting her reserve the tiny dog, but she insists that is the one she wants. Who am I to stand in the way of love? I carefully record her weight every couple of days to make sure that she is growing at a steady rate, and she is.

The puppies play in a large play pen outside the kitchen during the day, and it is very sad that on collection day there gradually become fewer and fewer puppies waiting. All the owners are very excited about their new arrivals, and will keep in touch via email sending me photos of the puppies in their new homes. It is a wonderful thing to provide people with such joy in their lives.

September is also the month for weaning lambs. They are big enough now to be separated from their mothers. It is preferable to leave the lambs where they are, in a familiar environment, and move the mothers somewhere else, preferably out of earshot. It is very important that the ewes have a restful time before they become pregnant again in November, or they will struggle through the winter.

As our two fields are not quite out of earshot we decide to put up a new fence between the two areas. This is the beginning of what will become an autumn of fencing. We have lots of work to do, enclosing the new land that we have bought from a neighbour. When the new fence is finished we move the ewes away from their lambs, and let them live on their own in the familiar environment of the hay meadow.

There is a bit of shouting and crying for the first couple of days, but soon all but one sheep and lamb settle down. One female lamb will not settle, she is determined to be with her mother. Unfortunately she is an expert wall jumper, and avoiding the new fence she vaults a series of high walls to be reunited with her mother. We separate them again and again, but she always finds a way back. There is no point in fighting this losing battle, either the lamb will have to be sold, or we will have to let her be. As she is one of our best lambs we decide to let her be. She does not appear to be drinking milk from her mother, and she is allowed to stay with her.

One of the lambs has a less enjoyable time being separated from her mother. I am not sure exactly what happens, but without showing any signs of illness she dies and is eaten overnight by a badger. It is possible to see by the bits that a predator leaves after eating what has devoured a lamb. This is very dispiriting, but part of farming life. We must accept it and carry on.

I begin to feed the Hebridean sheep and lambs a tiny amount of food every day, and catch one of their lambs with my crook each day to wean. It is not easy to gather the Hebrideans to wean them, as they are cross grazing with the Dexter Cattle grazing a large area of rough land. There is not really an easy place to catch them without restraining the cows in their holding area. It seems easier to quietly remove one lamb each day without any fuss. None of the lambs are sold yet; they are all still grazing happily and growing well.

September is the time for labelling up the wool bag to be collected and sent off to the Wool Board. The last of the rare breed fleeces are sold individually on eBay. This ensures that we will get a reasonable amount for each fleece.

My 'Introduction to Keeping Sheep' course runs during September and October. This is an adult education course that I devised for Cumbria County Council Adult Education. Learners come to Rusland for one day per week to have a classroom-based session about keeping sheep, before a practical task and assessment each week.

The courses are very affordable, and have attracted a wide range of learners. This year we have a retired gentleman who is thinking about keeping sheep, a married couple who already have sheep but would like to learn more, a man who is thinking about getting sheep and a lady who would like to learn more about sheep.

Our classroom sessions cover topics such as native breeds of sheep, the stratified sheep system in the UK, legal requirements for keeping sheep and the commons in Cumbria. The practical assessed tasks include trimming sheep's feet, holding sheep safely, administering medicine and gathering sheep into a pen.

One of the learners becomes enthused about keeping sheep, and buys five shearlings from me. These are the Shetland/Ryeland mules. I have bred these to be the ideal smallholder's sheep. They are a manageable size, but are chunky enough to produce a lamb with a good carcass if people want to produce their own meat. They have beautiful teddy bear like faces, and fleeces that are of a high quality and can be spun for crafts. Best of all they have the hardiness and easy lambing ability of the Shetland sheep.

He is pleased with his new sheep, and I am pleased to have the money to take to the Rough Fell breeding ewe sale. Unfortunately I have to clean the holiday cottage first, so Hector sets off for the breeding sheep sale in his car, while I deliver Fergus at school and then clean the holiday cottage before taking the sheep trailer to the auction.

My day does not go to plan. I have only one thing on my mind, and that is the breeding sheep sale, but when I arrive at the cottage it is clear that all is not well. In addition to the general mess the toilet seat has been snapped off, with no explanation.

I clean the cottage, leave a note saying I will replace the seat later and head off to the auction. I burst through the door into the upstairs viewing area of the auction and the first words I hear are 'Sold Meanwell'. I ask a breeder at the back that I recognise 'What have I bought?' and he looks at me blankly. I creep into the seat next to Hector and say, 'What have you bought?' His reply is "You won't like them." I understand this to mean that they are the type of sheep that Hector likes, with very white faces.

The next sheep in the ring have very dark faces, and they are from the same breeder that my Rough Diamond purchase was from. 'How much have you spent?' I ask Hector. There is no reply; he is concentrating on the sheep in the ring. 'I like those sheep, just buy them if we can afford it' I say. I sit there having no idea how much we have spent, and whether or not we can afford these sheep, but patiently sit on my hands and watch Hector bid for and buy the sheep.

I follow Hector out of the auction ring, apparently all our money must have been spent, and he explains what he has bought. Three very good, white faced sheep that were sold individually, and the sheep I wanted.

There is no time for lunch as we must take these sheep home and then collect Fergus from school. As I am driving to collect Fergus I receive a call to ask how long I am going to be with the replacement toilet seat as it is causing a lot of inconvenience. Bother, I had forgotten about that. I collect Fergus and then we head straight into Kendal to a large DIY store to buy a toilet seat. We arrive at the cottage at about 8pm. The holidaymaker is very dispirited, as she has just paid for a meal she was not happy with at a local pub. Fergus looks at her wide eyed and says 'We haven't had our tea yet' and I say, 'Actually I haven't had my lunch yet.'

That stops the complaint and the guests seem very pleased that a thirteen year old workman has replaced their toilet seat.

As well as selling the fleeces on eBay I am also selling knitted hats now that the seasons are changing. I knit hats from my own alpaca fibre, and a neighbour's wool from her Bluefaced Leicester sheep. These are advertised on Twitter and are sent all over the world to lovely customers.

This will help to pay for the sheep shearing and hay making, and also a fleece jumper for Ruby for the coming winter. A special fleece that can be put on after she has been working in snow, which will restore her core body temperature. Of course, we hope there is not a lot of snow, but we need to be prepared.

Most of the hats are sent to the USA. The plummeting pound following the Brexit vote makes them appear very reasonably priced to Americans, and I offer free worldwide postage. The hats are received by the Twitter followers after about a week in the post, and they post pictures of themselves wearing the hats in various locations. One Twitter follower, Erin in Georgia, sends me three hats that she has knitted, and some models she has made of my sheep. It is amazing the friendships that can be made by posting pictures of sheep on social media.

I see a Ryeland gimmer lamb that I like the look of advertised online, and have a day trip to Carlisle to collect her. It turns out that the sellers also breed Dexter cattle and I have an enjoyable day looking at their farm and stock.

The swallows leave. Winter is now on the way, and I still don't have my Basic Payment Scheme money that I expected to get last December. My field rents are due in

September, and I ask my MP Tim Farron for help. I see him at the Westmorland Show and he tells me that he has spoken to the Rural Payments Agency and hopefully the money will be coming soon. Frustrated by a lack of progress, I post photos of my tenancy agreements on Twitter saying that I will not be able to renew them due to the inefficiency of the Rural Payments Agency.

The tweets are retweeted, and I am contacted by someone in charge of public relations at the Rural Payments Agency, and with less than 24 hours to go until payment is needed for my field rents I receive my Basic Payment Scheme money. There is no time to post cheques, so I hand deliver cash around to my landlords and explain the whole saga to them. Nothing is ever simple.

Change is in the air, not only have the swallows left for warmer climes, and Mr Robin has returned on the very next day for the winter, but the riverbanks in the valley that were damaged during the December floods are being repaired. In order for the machinery to get access to the riverbank some trees have to be removed, and these are chopped up for wood for the fires next winter.

We have had the pleasure of attending a Diamond wedding and a Ruby wedding in September in the valley. At the Diamond wedding one of the comments is that there has been no finer place in which to live a life. We are disappointed when we hear that we have not been shortlisted for the farm in Northumberland, after all the effort of putting in a bid, but we cannot be disappointed with living our life here in the Rusland Valley.

October

Jessica Lofthouse, the 'curious traveller' who wrote a lot of travel books about North West England in the 1950s, said:

> Rusland in autumn is a dale to put the seal on beauty. Silver birches divesting themselves of their last orange-gold leaves stand on carpets bright as piles of new-minted half pennies. Wild cherries are like flame against black yews, and poplars stand naked with their yellow leaves about their feet. On the dale floor the old unclaimed acres of mossland are like a glowing tapestry woven of the crimson-claret of heather, the burnt-orange of bog myrtle, the golds and blond brightness of reed beds and tufty bushes about the margin are brown and tawny. But the beeches are the pride of Rusland, single trees showering golden rain, trunks silver against the grey green of rocky knoll, and colonnades of beeches like the arcading of some great cathedral.

This autumn is particularly spectacular, it is warm and colourful. There is very little wind and the beech trees retain their orange leaves that rustle gently, and warm air fills the valley. The grass does not stop growing; tractors work long into balmy evenings cutting grass. It is most unusually warm and calm in the valley.

The abundance of grass means that the lambs are piling on weight, but the rich diet is also causing them to have mucky bums. We spend a lot of time catching and cleaning lambs to stop them getting infested with flies and maggots.

The warm weather has also caused the ragwort to grow

more than usual. I had uprooted ragwort religiously for three years and had got rid of most of it, but this year it bursts from the fields and needs to be uprooted by hand.

The Rough Fell tup sale takes place at the beginning of October, we go to watch but we do not need to buy a tup this year. There is a show with several categories for the age and size of flock that the sheep has come from, and Hector is pleased that he immediately picks out the sheep that goes on to win the overall championship. I have arranged to buy some more Welsh Hill Speckle Faced sheep from a friend in Wales who is coming up for the sale, and we transfer these in the car park at the auction.

At the beginning of October our sheep-keeping course has a field trip to look at the land that we have bought, and discuss how we can improve it. The land is heavily infested with rushes in parts, and in order to contain the ponies to eat the rushes some walls must be rebuilt. I explain my plans to the students, and we discuss fell going flocks and hefting on the common. The students always seem to enjoy meeting up as a group and discussing hopes and dreams they have for their own futures.

We have a Countryside Stewardship grant to repair some of the walls, and Hector has a friend who wants to do the walling. There are 90 metres of wall gaps to be repaired, it is a big undertaking. The course participants have a look at the gaps, and envisage how it will look when the hay meadows are contained and rejuvenated. We will start rebuilding the walls in November.

The fencing is a more pressing issue. We must get our new fields contained if we are to put separate groups in them for tupping time, when the male sheep will be released to a group of ewes. Hector has two weeks off college for half term and he spends the entire two weeks fencing.

The first job is to knock the fence posts in. In accessible areas this can be done with a tractor and post knocker, then the wire stock fencing is attached to it. In each new field we are also making a sheep pen so that in every area we can catch the sheep easily. We must also ensure that each field has drinking water, a hayrack and a feed trough.

They are long, exhausting days holding, pulling and hammering. A line of barbed wire is put along the top of the fence, and this keeps pinging into our hands. The land is so rocky and undulating that a lot of the posts have to be knocked in by hand with a steel post knocker or sledge-hammer. It is frustrating work as nothing seems to be square or flat.

At the end of two weeks the fields are contained, although the gates are just held in place with string, and we will be ready for the tups. In future years we will apply for more boundary grants if these are still available, and plant hedging along the length of the fencing. These will provide corridors for wildlife, and also provide a windbreak for the animals in the field.

At the end of October we have a day at Wasdale Show. Very atypically for shows this year it is a gloriously sunny day. The setting for the show in the shadow of Kirk Fell and Great Gable is the most spectacular of any show, and the sheep pens have a most picturesque backdrop.

The only sheep shown here are locally bred Herdwick Sheep. The Herdwick Sheep Breeders Association provide a knowledgeable commentator to discuss the classes and the judging criteria. There are so many categories that it

Wasdale Show.

takes all day to judge. This year the judge is James Re-
banks, and I position myself behind the sheep pens sitting
by a wall with my border collie Moss and listen to the commentary.

It is one of those magical days that you would like to
preserve in your memory forever. The sheep, the shepherds
and the sunshine. Everything I am interested in is held
within the confines of this showfield.

My husband Antony runs in the fell race and comes a
brilliant third place. The fell race is a gut-busting climb and

exhilarating free-fall up and down Kirk Fell. It is a classic 'up and down' fell race that was first raced by the shepherds showing sheep at Wasdale. It has everything you could wish for in a fell race including a grandstand view for the spectators who can watch the drama of the race unfold from the showfield. Antony is in second place going up, but takes a wrong line when descending and comes home third.

As soon as the fell race is off the hounds follow, tearing across the field and leaping over the wall at the end. They

Wasdale Show - vintage tractors.

follow an aniseed trail and are called home by their enthu-
siastic owners with buckets of food.

I am not competing in the sheep show or fell race, but I
am competing in the 'non-working dog not from the show
area' class (only working dogs from the show area compete
as working dogs here), and the best shepherd's boots competition. I do not get a prize in either. The judge looks very
surprised when I enter the ring in the shepherd's boots competition, but another lady soon comes over to join me. Moss
does not seem disappointed at not winning; she is enjoying
her day out in the sun.

After the competitions the sheep show is still on going,
so Moss and I lie down in the grass to watch. Surprisingly
the champion sheep has an out of season lamb accompa-
nying her. All the shepherds pay great attention to each
other's tups, and discuss their good and bad points. Some
even spend their lunch hour there, watching tups moving
up and down the sheep pen area and seeing how they move.
These people are fascinated with their work and passionate
about breeding quality sheep. They are the best advert possible for Cumbria, and the crowd watching and learning
about Herdwick sheep is fascinated.

There are vintage tractors competing at the show and
unfortunately we exit the show behind a line of them. There
is no chance of getting past, and we slowly creep home ad-
miring the view. It has been a perfect day.

At the end of October we sell our first lambs this year.
The Rough Fell lambs make £27 and the Ryelands £19.
They are sold 'store' so that another farm can fatten them,
but even so it is not a good price.

Other income streams must always be explored, and

thankfully during October I am very busy working for Cumbria Wildlife Trust collecting seeds for the Kew Gardens Millennium seed bank.

A chance meeting with a friend from Cumbria Wildlife Trust on a lane in Rusland led to several days fascinating work. The trust had been asked to collect the seeds from various trees to store in the Kew Gardens millennium seedbank. We had to collect several thousand seeds, each variety of a named seed coming from five trees within a half-mile radius. As I understand it, this is because a well established group of trees, which pollinate each other, over time develop a particular 'type' in that locality. This local type may be resistant to a disease (e.g. ash dieback). In the case of an outbreak of the disease, the seeds stored at Kew can be used to establish new populations of disease resistant trees.

My job was to collect crab apples, sloes and hawthorn berries. Each tree had to be recorded with a GPS location, and a physical tag put onto the tree. A sample of a branch of a tree with fruit then had to be collected, pressed in a herbarium and sent to Kew.

One day two apprentices came to help collect the seeds and learn about how farming can work hand in hand with wildlife in the Lake District. It is a great opportunity for me to show them our dormouse corridor and explain how we are removing rushes so that we can regenerate traditional hay meadows.

At the end of October the weather is exceptionally warm. I eat my lunch in the fields and then have an afternoon nap in the sun with Ruby on my legs. At the back of my mind a voice says 'we will pay for this later', but for now we just enjoy the sunshine.

Andrea and Ruby, photograph by Suzanne McNally.

November

November in the Lake District is often a misty month, with cloud inversions in the mornings. Mist hangs in the valley bottoms. If you get up early, and climb or drive up out of the mist, the mountains above the mist look like a magical kingdom.

Our school run to Windermere includes travelling across Lake Windermere on the car ferry, weather permitting, and on November mornings the mist hovers above the lake like smoke. I have often been accused of 'photoshopping' my photographs when I post them on Twitter, but I honestly wouldn't know how to do that. I simply point my camera and record the beauty of the lake.

We get the 8am ferry from Sawrey to Bowness. We are usually the only passengers, although the ferry can carry eighteen cars and over 100 foot passengers. If the weather looks too windy or wild for the ferry to be running we can phone the ferry man before we leave home to see if it is in service, and drive around the lake if necessary. There has been a ferry across the lake for more than 500 years, the current ferry is a chain ferry, but previously the ferryboat was rowed across. A steam ferry was established in 1870. Travelling on the ferry generally feels very safe today, although there have been disasters. In 1635 48 passengers and several horses drowned when the ferry was overloaded with wedding guests.

We do not normally have much snow in November, but

after all the beautiful sunshine in October the weather breaks suddenly and overnight autumn turns into winter on 9 November. There is a covering of snow in the valley bottoms and a great deal of snow on the mountains. Local tradition dictates that there will always be a light dusting of snow on the Langdale Pikes on 11 November for Remembrance Day, but this year it is more than a dusting. Winter has come early and hard to Cumbria.

The tups are put in with the ewes on 3 November this year. My 40 Rough Fell ewes have my tup, and Hector's ten have his tup. The Welsh Hill Speckle Faced sheep go to visit to a neighbour who has a Speckle tup. The Shetlands are in a new field with the Ryeland tup, and the Hebrideans are still cross grazing with the Dexters and have another Ryeland tup with them.

The Ouessants have their tup with them, and after the experience at lambing time the shearlings are not put to the tup this year. They will have to grow on for another year. I realise that I will be able to keep my Ouessant tup for three years instead of two, when his daughters will be coming into the flock. I like my current Ouessant tup so this is definitely a plus point.

The tups have a thick oily mixture called raddle applied to their chests. This makes a mark when they mate with a ewe. We can see that each tup is working and we can record when each ewe should be due. My neighbour rings me each time a Speckle is marked so I can make a note of the date. There are bits of paper with cryptic messages on everywhere.

Feeding must begin in earnest because of the weather, and my daily winter round of feeding begins again. This

Hector tub daubing.

will be my routine every day until the grass starts to grow in the spring. The frosts are hard and the ground becomes frozen. Our lips become chapped and our cheeks burn when we come indoors into the warm kitchen.

The Rayburn stove is lit in the kitchen and that too must be fed like an animal; logs that have been cut and stored from around the farm are fed into the stove every couple of hours. The air source heat pump provides hot water.

November is traditionally seen as the start of the fell farming year, and with the tups in with the ewes and feeding rounds begun again there is regularity and rhythm to each day. There is a growing realisation that winter is upon us and must be endured. We must work hard, keep our heads down and hope for the best as far as the weather is concerned.

At this time of year I find that winter feeding occupies my whole being, mental and physical. There is no time or energy to consider anything else. As long as everyone is fed, watered, exercised, healthy and happy everything is alright. I am not dreaming of holidays in the sun, or worrying about future plans, I am simply getting through each day. Each day is a day nearer to lambing time. My goal is to have fields full of lambs and calves in the summer, and a garden full of puppies. This is the time to put in the physical work that will achieve these results.

One misty morning I wake up to the telephone ringing, and the news that one of the valley's much loved residents has died. I look out of my bedroom window along the valley bottom; the mist hangs heavily shrouding the valley as it mourns. There is a palpable, physical feeling to the shock and sadness that all the residents feel, and the valley seems to be echoing our mood. It may be a fanciful notion, but as we all go about our business meeting each other sadly on the lanes and exchanging memories, it seems that the valley itself has gone into mourning.

It is as if the wonderful autumn colours this year were putting on a show before our much loved neighbour left us, and now the valley itself is cloaking itself in thick mist and sadness. Like the snow on the Langdales on 11 November each year as we remember the fallen of two world wars and conflicts, it is as if our human and physical experiences have somehow become bound up with the very landscape of the Lake District itself.

I continue selling lambs, a few each fortnight and get similar prices each time, between £24 and £27 for the Rough Fells and around £19 for the Ryelands. This income keeps us 'ticking over' and pays for the winter feed that is now required.

During November we begin rebuilding the interior walls on our land in the Crake Valley. While the exterior walls are kept up, the interior walls have been neglected for many years. They are half standing, and half spread across the fields and overgrown with years of grass growth.

By rebuilding these walls we can separate what is currently one big area of rough grazing into four smaller fields. One of these fields will be a hay meadow, the others need to have the rushes that have infested them eaten by the fell ponies, and the drains re-dug. A second field can then be rejuvenated as a hay meadow as it was traditionally.

The Countryside Stewardship grant to reinstate the walls is run by Natural England. Each bit of wall that is repaired has to be photographed, measured and mapped

Feeding cattle, photograph by Suzanne McNally.

before the repair can be agreed with Natural England.

We are pleased to have one of Hector's friends coming to work for us on Saturday and Sunday to do the walling. He works solidly throughout the day, and has to be encouraged to even stop for lunch. At the end of the first weekend I am astonished when Hector tells me that his friend has already done his usual Saturday job, starting at 5.30am feeding sheep, so that he can be with us by 9am to start walling. For the first weekend he removes all the overgrown stones by hand with a pickaxe, but requests the hire of a mini digger for the second weekend to speed the process up. The foundation stones of the wall are not disturbed, in case any wildlife has made a home there. We have a lot of slow worms overwintering on our land, and they may be hibernating in the wall bottoms. Seeds such as foxgloves can also use the wall as shelter to allow them to germinate.

I had thought it would take months to repair the walls, but by the end of the first month real progress has been made, and it is hoped that this set of fields can be finished by Christmas. It is great to see the walls standing tall again. It is very sad to see tumbledown walls that have not been rebuilt. It is a huge effort keeping walls up in the Lake District, but it maintains the landscape that thousands of visitors know and love. It also makes the land much more useful for us.

November is also the month of the red deer rut in the valley. Daylight is in short supply, and our evening school runs are done after dark. Driving about the valley becomes a bit like a video game where you never know when something will leap out at you. One evening we encounter three separate groups of young stags chasing each other and leaping across the road in front of the car. The valley also echoes with Scooby Doo type noises coming from the Rusland Mosses at night as the stags roar to state their dominance over the herd.

There is not a lot of educational work around during the winter, but one November day I am asked to meet 90 children from Morecambe aged between five and seven, and teach them about nocturnal animals for Cumbria Wildlife Trust. We agree to meet at Brockhole, the Lake District National Park's Visitor Centre, and I take three groups of 30 in turn to discuss bats and badgers and their habitats. It is a brilliantly clear ice cold morning and the children have fun breaking the ice in puddles. They shriek with delight when they realise they can pick it up 'It's not glass, Miss, is it?' and nobody complains once about the cold.

Half way through one workshop a small boy comes over to me and says: 'I am crying Miss.'

'Oh no' I say, 'what's wrong?'

'Happy tears Miss, because I have never been in the country like this before.'

In that moment it became worth getting up at 5.30am to feed the animals so that I could meet these children for the day. What a privilege it is to be able to have such experiences with them.

I also have a moment of awe and wonder myself when my husband runs in a fell race at Arnside and I go to watch. I walk down to the beach and there is not a breath of wind. The whole panorama of Morecambe Bay with the Lake District fells snow capped in the distance behind is breath taking. What an amazing place Cumbria is, we are truly blessed to live here.

December

The first day of December is census day in the sheep keeping world. Like Mary and Joseph on their way to Bethlehem to be counted, we must make our own journey around all our sheep on 1st December recording breeding sheep and lambs for the Rural Payments Agency. This is part of a process called 'cross compliance' which farmers must adhere to in order to receive their Basic Payment Scheme payment. Coincidentally, the payment window for the 2016 scheme opens today, and on social media some farmers are delighting in the fact that they have got their 2016 payments. Cumbrian farmers, meanwhile, are still waiting for some of our 2015 payment due to the 'too complicated to calculate' system of commons in Cumbria.

After the census I am ready on 1st December to set off for the auction with a trailer full of lambs, but the Land Rover will not start. It has been threatening to break down for about a week now, and of course on the morning I want to go somewhere it decides to break down at the most inconvenient time.

The lambs are put back into the shed, they will have to wait another week longer eating hay and cake indoors. They do not seem too troubled by this. I am troubled, however, by a heavy cold/flu and the last thing I needed was the Land Rover breaking down.

My neighbour, also full of cold, arrives with jump leads, but we decide that we must call out the mechanic in the next village. He arrives from further along the valley, and by lunchtime the Land Rover is fixed, at minimal cost, by a local business. It is a wonderful thing that we still have small businesses supporting each other in this quiet area of the Lake District. If I had to take the Land Rover to the main dealership to be repaired the cost would be prohibitive for such a small farm as mine.

It is too late, however, for the sale. I must content myself with counting sheep. I know, of course, which sheep are where, but I tend to remember groups of faces and not numbers. If you ask me how many sheep are in a particular field I would say 'Well, there's Squiggle and her sister and their two daughters, and that odd black-faced one, and Hector's three from Tebay plus last year's orphan lambs.' I wouldn't equate this with a 'number' in my head. Today, however, it is all about numbers. The numbers are entered online at lunchtime and an email is sent to say that I have complied with that legal requirement.

I can go back to bed before the afternoon jobs need to be done. There is no chance of a 'sick day' on a hill farm. You can have a day when only the bare essentials are done, but you cannot stay in bed all day unless you have someone to help you out. I have even been known to drive the Land Rover around the valley checking sheep stopping every couple of minutes to be sick, once right outside a neighbour's kitchen window – many apologies.

The lambs have to wait two weeks until the next store lamb sale. This seems to suit the Ryeland crosses who get happily fat inside, but the Rough Fells do not take so well to being indoors. They are fell sheep, and do not thrive indoors, rather like me!

By the date of the sale I can see that they do not look brilliant, their coats are thick with hay, but I take them all anyway. It is the first day of the Christmas holidays for Fergus, and he comes to the auction to help me sell them. He is smartly dressed in a shirt and tie, and is very helpful reversing the Land Rover into the loading bays at the auction mart that I find very tricky.

We watch some of the lots being sold, and meet a neighbour who tells us everything is 'five pounds down a head'. Not a good sign. It is also apparent from watching that every time horned sheep come into the ring less people are interested in bidding. The horned fell breeds have a slower growing carcass than many of the commercial sheep, and are not so much of a 'money maker' for the buyer of store lambs to fatten for the meat market.

We dash back downstairs from watching the sale and are there just in time, our lambs are the next ones in the ring. I have a very hurried conversation with the staff, who tell me to split up the Rough Fell sheep in order to get a better price. The first ones in the ring get £25.50, the medium sized £21 and we struggle to get bids on the smaller lambs. I will not sell them at a loss, and so make a split second decision to take them home again. The Ryelands sell for £22.50.

Once back at home the smaller Rough Fells go back outside with a high energy feed bucket, and soon have a spring in their step again. It was a mistake to keep them indoors. We live and learn.

Throughout December I promote my knitwear as much as I can without boring people on Twitter. This is a valuable income stream for the farm. I sell hand-knitted hats at £20 including postage anywhere in the world. The wool I am using is Bluefaced Leicester and Castlemilk Moorit wool from a farm in the Crake Valley along with my own alpaca fibre for the rim of the berets. This is because the alpaca fibre is hypoallergenic and not at all scratchy, making the hats very comfortable. People seem very pleased with the hats and post pictures of themselves wearing them all over the world when they have arrived in the post. Some customers return to buy more products, and it is great to build up a friendship with people who love your products and want to support your farm.

At the beginning of December the government puts restrictions in place regarding the keeping of poultry because of the threat of avian flu. The hens are all put in a shed, and will have to stay there for 30 days. The geese are put into a loose box in the stable. While this is not pleasant denying the poultry their freedom, it certainly makes life easier over Christmas when I will not feel anxious about staying away from home after dark. If I am out at dusk I worry that a fox will come.

Daily feeding routines continue, at this time of year there is also a lot of coming and going in the holiday let. Lots of people come to the cottage before Christmas, often to visit relations who live here, and there are a lot of changeovers to do. The animals are happily eating hay and for the most part are settled in the rough grazing for the winter, but there are three nagging problems and I won't be able to relax until they are solved.

One is that the ponies need to see the farrier to have their feet trimmed, and there is one pony that will not be caught. She missed seeing the farrier last time as she refused to come in then, and I am worried about her feet as they are very overgrown. The ponies do not wear shoes; their feet are regularly trimmed by the farrier. This pony, Apple, has an entirely different personality once she realises that she has been caught, and has her head collar on. For this reason she usually wears a head collar every day, but she has lost her current one and will not let me anywhere near her to put another one on.

Patience and perseverance pay off. Throughout the month of December I call the ponies over every morning to eat a little hay. With the friendlier ponies I groom and brush them while they eat, and Apple observes this, and sees that the other ponies are not troubled by it. After two weeks of doing this I attempt to brush her as well. On the third day of trying she lets me groom her, and I brush her mane and rub her back each day. After several more days I then introduce the idea of a head collar, by getting one out of my pocket and letting her smell it as I groom her. She takes an interest in this, and on the third day of producing it out of my pocket she lets me put it on. I am so relieved that she will be able to get her feet trimmed now. It is awful to feel that you are not looking after an animal properly and not doing your best for her.

The second problem is that some of the lambs and Hebridean sheep have evaded capture and are still in their summer pasture. Again patience must be used. I feed them every morning and gradually coax them into a very small field and shut them in there. The field has a sheep pen in the corner. I know that by putting their food in there I will gradually coax them all in and be able to catch them.

Patience pays off again and after two weeks I have

moved them all into the rough grazing with the other rare breeds. It is pointless trying to use a dog with them, as they can outrun a dog and this is not ideal when they are pregnant. Moss is used to catch up any remaining lambs that are alone without their pregnant mothers, and Ruby is used each day to make sure that all the lambs are brought down

Feeding the fell ponies, photograph by Suzanne McNally.

for food. Any lambs that ignore me calling are shepherded down to the hayrack by Ruby to get the hang of eating hay. There is simply not enough grass to keep them going at this time of year. Ruby also guides them over to the lick bucket that contains minerals, and the lambs soon learn to love these.

The final problem is that we have a tuberculosis (TB) test booked for the 20 and 23 December, and we must get all the cows and calves in for this. Again, patience is the key and for the whole of December I walk the cows into the holding area to feed them. The two calves are not keen on this, but usually come in after a few minutes. By the third week of December they are used to coming into the holding area and Hector confidently tells me 'We are going to have no trouble at all with them.'

The test is necessary because someone locally bought a calf on a 'linked holding', actually 40 minutes drive from our house, and this calf was found to have TB. We have all now been subjected to regular TB testing, and no TB has been found in the valley. If all our December tests are clear we can all go back to a four-year testing regime that will be a huge relief. I do not want to be the person to mess up the testing regime and delay this happening.

Perhaps the calves can sense our anxiety, or perhaps it is because my landlord is walking his dog in the field that morning, but for one reason or another on 20 December the calves will not come in. The test is booked for 9.30am, and when the vet arrives I tell him what has happened. Not phased, he tells me to shut the other cows in half of the holding area and he will go and do somebody else's TB test and come back. He is confident that the calves will come to their mothers.

I do this, and hide behind a tree waiting for the calves to go in. They are now quite happily grazing about half a mile away from the holding area, ignoring the anxious cries of their mothers. The calves carry on grazing, oblivious.

When the vet comes back he is very surprised that the calves have not come in, and says not to worry, we will herd them in. Neighbours come to help, and we try to push the calves along with a combination of people and dogs. There is no way that these calves are going to go in. It seems pointless to try.

'What happens now?' I ask the vet.

'I don't know, this has never happened before' he replies, and I feel really stupid wondering how long he has been a vet, and how many thousands of TB tests he has done with competent farmers and compliant cows.

'I feel really stupid and incompetent,' I say.

'I just feel sorry for you, because I am going to have to charge you when I come back,' says the vet. He reassures me that it will be alright to test the calves at a later date, as long as it is within the permitted window.

'What happens if I cannot get them in by January?' I ask my neighbour.

'It's OK' he says. 'We can move them to slaughter without a TB test. I will bring my shotgun.' He collapses in hysterics and I realise thankfully that he is joking, but I still do not know what will happen if we cannot catch them.

We leave the calves for a couple of days to settle down. Thankfully the cows all pass their TB test. I now need to think of a way to catch the calves, but meanwhile it is almost Christmas and I have a cottage changeover on

23 December, after the TB test, and animal jobs to do on Christmas Eve morning. On Christmas Eve afternoon there is time for Christmas shopping, and thankfully everything I have on a very long list is available. Antony is waiting at the door for the ingredients when I return; ready to start preparing Christmas dinner. Unfortunately I did not enjoy the shopping as the wind blew the car door into the side of my head, and much of the afternoon was a daze after that.

On returning home I get a series of Twitter notifications telling me that my first book *A Native Breed* has arrived at customers' houses in time for Christmas. The book was published on 16 December and posted from France for those who had pre-ordered, and I am very relieved that it has arrived in time to be popped into Christmas stockings.

My eldest son Oscar is home from university and is farm sitting for some neighbours who have gone to visit relatives in South Africa for Christmas, so that night I drive him up to the farm on the fell and he spends Christmas Eve alone there. As we drive up to house I say to him 'I'm sure I just saw a pony in that field' (not one of their fields), and their ponies have knocked down a fence and escaped. Thankfully he is in charge of dogs, cats, poultry and cows, but not ponies, so he can telephone someone else to come and erect some electric fencing as a temporary measure.

Christmas Day is not quite the torrential washout that was forecast, although we feel that we are blown along to church like ships in full sail. Most of our neighbours are there, along with some Christmas holiday visitors, and we enjoy singing carols and having a quick mince pie before jumping into the Land Rover and straight off to feed the sheep.

It is not easy to explain, but there is always something special about feeding animals on Christmas Day. I guess that the best way to describe it is that it is an absolute privilege to work in these valleys with beautiful animals 365 days a year, and my heart sings that I can do this on Christmas Day a little louder than on other days of the year. I used to love Christmas morning in the cow byre with my neighbour when I was helping him with his heifers. Do the cows know its Christmas? Of course, they will kneel down at midnight as the old story tells.

Christmas dinner is served after all the animal jobs have been completed at 3pm and thankfully we have no injuries, illnesses or challenges to deal with which would delay our dinner. My parents come over for lunch. Unusually we do not have a neighbour joining us this year. Nobody eats alone at Christmas in Rusland.

After dinner it is back outside to walk the dogs before bedtime, and Christmas Day is over for another year. I know Christmas was made as a midwinter festival to cheer people up at this time of year, but as the main festival of the year it always seems spectacularly badly timed to me. There is so little daylight to get the work done, never mind feasting as well.

The holiday cottage visitors only stay until Boxing Day, and there is another booking from 3pm for New Year, so the cottage must be cleaned the following day and made to look lovely and festive again.

Leaving aside the problem of the calves, there is another nagging issue that is on everyone's mind at the end of the year. That is the issue of finding a larger farm. As both attempts to get a rented farm have been unsuccessful, we have come to the momentous decision that we will have to sell our house (not necessarily our land) to find a larger farm.

On New Year's Eve we travel to Hawes in North Yorkshire to look at two farms. Lovely as Hawes is, it does not feel like home to us. North Yorkshire definitely feels like another country! We enjoy our visit to Hawes, but decide it is probably not somewhere we could move to.

We also look at a farm in the Howgill Fells, and this fires our imagination. We have plans a plenty, and can imagine ourselves living there with our Rough Fell sheep. The previous owners have had 1,600 Rough Fell sheep on the farm. It also comes with amongst other things, a Roman fort and another ruined farmstead. The future looks challenging... if only I can catch those blasted calves!

Early morning, before sunrise on New Year's Day 2017, and I guess there will not be a lot of traffic going past our house before dawn. Before it gets light an elaborate pulley system has been set up close to the gate to trap the calves, and food placed as bait. I park the Land Rover out of sight, and then crawl along the roadside so the calves cannot see me over the wall. I get hold of the rope attached to the gate, and lie on the road not moving a muscle or making a sound. It begins to rain. The sun comes up. Time passes. Two cars go by and I do not make eye contact with them. This is the closest to espionage I will ever get, and I wonder if any spies are currently staking out premises like I am staking out my calves.

I hear mooing, and the sound of cows coming down the hill. The older cows will hopefully come into the holding area and the younger ones will follow, thinking I am not around. I cannot see which cows are in the holding area, but I can hear them eating. I say to myself over and over 'one chance, one chance' and when I am ready I spring up and see the calves in the holding area (YES!) and pull the rope. The gate pulls closed to the gate post, the cows could still barge the gate and snap the rope if they want to, so quick as a flash I leap over the wall and into the holding area, so that they all move to the other end away from the gate.

I shut the gate, jump back out, and lie on the road with the rain pouring onto me, splashing my face. I laugh and laugh and laugh some more. I laugh until my cheeks ache, and then begin to run home, collecting the Land Rover on the way, to share the news. What an absolute relief!

Afterword

I hope that you enjoyed reading about a year *In My Boots*. It has been a year of getting soaked to the skin, following on from the floods of December 2016. There have also been droughts and a shortage of grass to contend with. We never know what sort of challenges the weather will have in store for us.

Problems have arisen and been solved. We have learnt from some mistakes, and will no doubt make many more mistakes in the future as we build our business. There is never a time in the year that is not challenging, and for that I am very thankful. We have been very busy, there is an old saying 'If you want something doing ask a busy person.' We have been full of busy, full of doing. Long may it continue.

Thankfully the calves passed their TB test on 5 January, and we were put back onto a four year testing regime. The steer calf, who had been the chief culprit in the shenanigans, was sold to a farm in the Yorkshire Dales where they fatten pedigree Dexter calves for gourmet chefs. Primrose, his partner in crime, was retained in the herd as a breeding heifer.

At the time of writing we are coming up to lambing time and fully absorbed in our winter feeding regime. I am dreaming of lambing time, a thought that gets me up early on dark winter mornings to load the Land Rover with food. This year is the first year that our homebred Rough Fell ewes will be lambing themselves, and we will really see what our future flock looks like. I can't wait.

A Moment's Sadness

At times like these
I allow myself
Just a moment's sadness

A moment's sadness
Washes through me
From top to bottom

Then I steel myself
To move and dispose
Of the body

Sadness acknowledged
Practicalities take over
Jobs to do

If I let the sadness
Linger in my heart
I would be ended.

Hope in a Handful

A handful of hope
A newborn lamb
Wriggling with potential

New life
Bursting with promise
Brings optimism

Happiness
Hope for the future
Joy in a handful

Keep hold of the joy
Hold it in my heart
Throughout winter

That joy will be there
To use when required
To get me through.

Acknowledgements

This book owes its existence to my publisher Dawn Robertson at Hayloft books. Thank you Dawn for believing in the book, and thinking it a valuable story to tell and share. Thanks also to Suzanne McNally for again taking some fantastically atmospheric photos for the book, and to Celine Mathé and Sarah Voulleminot who helped with the photographs.

Thank you to my parents, husband and children for their commitment to our farming projects. This book also owes its existence to the ambition of my sons. In September 2015, after winning the English fell running championships, my oldest son Oscar represented England at the World Mountain Running Championships in Snowdonia. He came fourth, and the English team won. After seeing him on the podium I said that if I never had another day in my life feeling as proud as that it wouldn't matter. My youngest son then told me not to worry, I would feel proud, as he intended to sail in the Tera World Sailing Championships the following year.

There then followed several months of intensive sailing training, Fergus was out on the water for up to five hours at a time, whilst I sat in a sailing club lounge or in the car waiting. I determined to make the most of the time by writing this book. A great debt of gratitude is also owed to Hector, who looked after our various animals whilst we went off sailing, especially when we left him for a week to go to the World Championships. Special thanks to my husband who supported us with our farming, and fed us after long days outside with his fantastic cooking.

Thank you to everybody who has rented me land, and to the community of farmers in the Rusland and Crake Valleys who have helped me with both advice and practical tasks. Raymond Crowe and John Park have both helped me so much with my animals over the last six years, and we have had a lot of laughs together.

Thank you to my twitter followers @ruslandvalley whose kind comments are always a source of inspiration, and encouragement to produce this second book. It is good to know that you enjoyed the first book, and have been looking forward to the second. I hope it met with your expectations. Thank you also to the readers of my column in *Cumbria* magazine.

Last but not least, thank you to you the reader. I hope the book was enjoyable and entertaining. We have a lot of plans and optimism for the future of our family farm, and I hope to share them with you in the future.

References

T. S. Eliot, *The Waste Land*, 1922, Faber and Faber.
Jessica Lofthouse, *The Curious Traveller: Lancaster to Lakeland,* 1956, Hale.

Books by the Same Author

A Native Breed, Starting a Lake District Hill Farm
(2016)